Nourish Your Body

A 30-DAY HEALTHY & DELICIOUS MEAL PLAN

Renata Trebing

NOURISH WITH RENATA

n

nutrition & energy

Nourish Your Body: A 30-Day Healthy & Delicious Meal Plan
Published by Nourish with Renata Publications
Houston, Texas
USA

www.nourishwithrenata.com

Contact publisher for bulk orders and permission requests.

Cover and interior book design & formatting by
Leesa Ellis of 3 ferns books ➤ **www.3fernsbooks.com**

Photography by Renata Trebing

Printed in the United States of America.

Library of Congress Control Number: 2021940150

ISBN: 978-05789125-5-4

Contents

Week 1

Week 2

Week 3

Week 4

This book is dedicated to my family

Cody, Olivia, Harrison, Dean, and June.
I love you all so much.

As well as...

Every woman who goes above and beyond for others but sometimes forgets to nourish herself. This book is your how-to guide on filling your own cup, literally and figuratively. When we show up for ourselves, when we fuel and nourish our bodies every day, we are able to show up as our best selves for others too. We also set an example to those around us, that nourishing our bodies, also nourishes our minds and souls. It is a daily practice and how we can show ourselves the greatest form of self-care and love.

Foreword

From the moment I met Renata through a business networking group, I knew that she would have a positive impact on my life. I have never met someone so excited about food!

Not long after I met her, I asked her if she designed meal plans. She answered with a resounding "Yes!" I was so excited to hear this. I was bored with my chicken dinners with a side of broccoli, seasoned (and I use that term lightly) only with salt and pepper. On special occasions I would break out the "chicken seasoning" and really mix it up! Boring food is boring. I wasn't feeling excited to make dinner, I had cookbooks with complicated recipes and hard-to-find ingredients and it became so much easier to order-in.

What I quickly found through working with Renata is that because my food wasn't tasty and there was no variety, I wasn't eating enough or feeling satiated after meals. I would often find myself grazing the kitchen for something else even though I had eaten what seemed to be a complete meal.

Renata's menus changed my meals instantly! The use of spices (who knew cinnamon could be so powerful?), the balance of nutrients and the deliciousness were so much more than I had imagined. To me, it was like food I could have in a restaurant from the comfort of my own home. Besides the incredible flavor, they are easy to prep, cook and – my favorite part – enjoy! Still to this day "Egg Roll in a Bowl" has to be my go-to on those nights when I just feel like a tasty, filling, super-easy meal. (What page is that one on, Renata?)

Fast forward to today, in which Renata has become a dear friend whose success I celebrate. I can't wait for you to browse the recipes and find the ones that stretch you to think about cooking a little bit differently.

Anne L. Laguzza

Introduction

Have you ever thought to yourself "I shouldn't have eaten that"? Have you ever felt guilty about eating a so-called "bad" food?

It's like food had suddenly derailed you from your plans to live as the ultimate health and wellness guru and your whole day was ruined?

I hear ya!

I have definitely been there. And it's the worst feeling in the world.

Not just because you feel guilty because you ate it, but because your body feels sluggish, bloated and, for lack of a better term, gross.

If you're anything like me, you'd then punish your body for eating the "bad" food. I'd workout incessantly or try to starve myself or force myself to only have green juice for a week.

Would it work? Heck no! In fact, I'd feel even more deprived and then I'd go off the deep end and eat every candy, cupcake and pie in sight.

I finally got to the point where I couldn't treat my body like this anymore. The constant rollercoaster of food and emotions, of bingeing and attempted deprivation was simply not working.

I had to find a way to eat that was both healthy and delicious. A place where I could have healthy indulgences and not fall into the loop of guilt and overeating; where I could feel proud of myself, my food and my choices, each and every day.

I started by experimenting with food to find out what foods actually helped me feel good; what foods fueled and nourished my body. And what I found was actually not surprising at all.

Eating whole foods, or minimally processed foods, made me feel energized, full of life and vitality. I didn't feel bloated and I was able to accomplish all the things I wanted to during the day.

Armed with this new-found information, I started creating delicious and healthy recipes that fit into my new way of eating.

I was so excited about these recipes and shared them (aka shamelessly tested them) on my family. Sure, there were some recipes they didn't love, but the ones they did, those recipes were keepers!

I made these recipes for friends and other family. Soon they were asking me for these recipes so they could make them at home too.

That's when I knew I had to share them with the world.

So, I started the **NourishwithRenata.com** blog. In this blog, I share healthy and delicious recipes, as well as healthful tips and tricks to help you move towards your healthiest version of you.

Now, years later, I coach women on how to fuel their bodies to feel their best. I've put my recipes together into meal plans, to guide them on what to eat and when.

These meal plans have helped women feel more confident in the kitchen as well as in their bodies. The recipes have taught women how to cook fast, easy and tasty food. These meal plans have also helped women not only lose weight and inches, but finally feel like they are completely satiated and nourished.

And that's why I am bringing my meal plans to you.

This cookbook is a 30-Day Healthy Meal Plan to get you started living your healthiest and happiest life. If you've been waiting to start your healthy living journey, this is your sign! And I'm honored to guide you along the way.

In this book, I will walk you through recipes for all your meals and snacks, as well as some options for store-bought alternatives.

I'll throw in some tips and tricks to help you make this lifestyle change sustainable for you and your family, without sacrificing time or flavor.

Now I know that there may be times when you'll want to go out with your family to a restaurant or it's someone's birthday party or you're going on a quick weekend vacation. How do you stay on track when these events happen?

Don't worry!

I've written a whole chapter on what to do when eating out to help arm you with tools to help you feel in control of these situations.

Lastly, this is not an all or nothing plan. This cookbook is a guide. Of course, with consistency, you can bring new, positive and sustainable habits into your life. But I'm not a drill sergeant! I understand that sometimes life happens and we fall a little further away from where we'd like to be. Always remember that the next choice you make is exactly that; YOUR CHOICE. Your next choice is your opportunity to choose to move closer to your goals, towards the healthiest, happiest and most nourished you.

As always, if you have any questions, reach out to me on social media! I love to answer your questions and help you on your road to living your healthiest, happiest and most nourished life!

Renata

Follow me on social media
Instagram: @nourish_with_renata
Facebook: http://www.facebook.com/getnourishedwithrenata

Emotional connection to food, aka Can I ever have cake again???

It would be totally foolish to think that you can change how you eat and never get tempted again. The truth is that there is a huge emotional connection to food. Food is often something that brings families and friends together. It is how we celebrate and how we console. It is how we show love and how we comfort each other. So, instead of becoming robots to an overly strict diet, the key to sustainable healthy eating is to:

Recognize that there IS an emotional connection to food.

And realize that it is OK to enjoy your time, and food, with your loved ones.

There are always going to be times when there are birthday parties and celebrations, where there will be cake and chocolate (my fave!). You always have a choice if you want to have some of these celebration foods, or not.

And if you do, please understand this;. one piece of cake, or one candy bar, is NOT going to derail you from living a healthy life. A constant series of choices to have these foods will derail you. But one time, one choice to eat food with your family, will not.

Like I said before, your next choice can move you closer to being the person you want to be.

The 80/20 rule

What is the 80/20 rule? This easy way of looking at food encourages no food deprivation... yay! It is a fantastic way to think about food. This old adage says we should aim to eat healthy 80% of the time, and the remaining 20% is for eating those foods you may be craving but shouldn't be having regularly. When you approach food like this, it doesn't make you overindulge in guilty pleasures because you always know that you can have those foods at any time, just by using the 80/20 rule.

Threshold

Ever felt really gross and bloated after you've gone to town on a cheese board? Or maybe you start feeling sleepy after you've eaten too much bread?

I like to call this **Exceeding the Threshold.** With a lot of foods that may cause inflammation, such as gluten, dairy, and soy, there is a limit to how much you can eat before you start feeling the adverse effects like bloating, lethargy, and tiredness.

So, if you have reduced or eliminated these inflammatory foods from your diet during the next 30 days, you might find that you can slowly introduce these foods back into your diet to a limited extent. If you go past this limit, or threshold, you might start to experience the bloating, gas, and/or lack of energy again.

Knowing that there is a threshold can empower you to make choices by knowing what the potential outcomes will be of your decisions. It can also help you feel at ease because you don't have to necessarily cut out anything from your eating plan, you just eat an amount lower than the threshold and you will still feel good.

How the 30-Day Meal Plan works

The next 30 days of recipes are based upon whole foods and I don't mean Whole Foods the store! I mean whole fruits, vegetables, lean proteins, and healthy fats.

The aim with this 30-Day Meal Plan is to reduce the potentially inflammatory ingredients that you're eating, and to increase the goodness that comes from unrefined, wholesome ingredients.

Most often, we are so used to eating potentially inflammatory foods that we don't even realize the effect that it is having on our bodies. You may recognize some symptoms of inflammation as bloating, swelling in other body parts, brain fog, an irritated digestive system, to name just a few. So, during these 30 days, let's focus on increasing lots of whole food ingredients so we can feel our absolute best.

Each week, I will provide a Week At A Glance summary of the meals for the week. This summary table will also show some vegan options for each and every meal. Note that this is just a guide. You can choose to follow this meal plan to a T, or swap days around based upon what works best for you and your family. That is totally OK! Find what works best for you and your loved ones.

This 30-Day Meal Plan was created with one meal prep strategy in mind: **Make One More.** This means that when you walk into the kitchen to make a salad for lunch, use that time to make one more salad for tomorrow (without the dressing so it doesn't get soggy!) You can use this strategy for lots of the meals on this meal plan. This strategy is very simple to use when you are just starting out meal prepping. That is also why I have the same menu for two days e.g. Monday and Tuesday have the same menu. If you are well versed in meal prepping, feel free to meal prep for multiple days or the whole week. Do what works best for you and your family!

I will also provide a shopping list for each week. This will help to keep you organized and on track with your grocery store shopping. The grocery lists assume you don't have common pantry staples, such as salt, pepper, oil etc. But if you do, feel free not to purchase any more of that ingredient and use what you have.

Also, if there are any ingredients in the recipe that you don't love, feel free to swap them for some ingredients you do love, or adjust the recipe based upon the ingredients you have.

Listen to Your Body

Here is one key to getting the most from this 30-Day Meal Plan: **Listen to Your Body.**

It is so easy for us to ignore the cues our body tell us. Anyone else continued to eat something even though they were full but it just tasted sooo good? Oh yeah, I've been there too.

What I'd love for you to practice during these 30 days, is to be mindful of how your body feels after a meal. Making a note of how your body feels after eating something, is what I call a Food Log. This is a much more flexible version of a food log than you may have heard of in the past. My kind of Food Log is just a way for us to make a note of how food impacts our energy levels, brain fog, and digestive system. You can get a handy, travel-sized Food Log Journal at NourishWithRenata.com.

Ultimately, getting into the practice of writing down how you feel after you eat something, will provide clues to let us know what foods are fueling you, versus what foods are draining you of energy. And, obviously, we want to focus on the fueling foods the majority of the time. We just need to have a good idea first, of what those foods are.

Foods that Fuel Us

What do I mean when I say this? I am referring to foods that give us energy, help us feel our best, and don't cause any inflammation in the body.

Most often, my clients feel their best when they are eating 80% whole foods, meaning fruits, veggies, lean proteins and healthy fats from whole foods sources, such as avocados, and nuts/ seeds.

Of course, this doesn't mean that you are never allowed to have cake or chocolate again! In fact, I actually recommend occasionally having some of your favorite comfort foods. Why? Because there is a huge emotional component to food. Think about any major holiday or celebration. There was likely a bunch of food there and everyone ate to their heart's content.

This is completely normal. There are going to be times when we are with family and friends, and we want to indulge a little. I never want you to feel deprived; instead, I would love for you to feel mindful.

Think about why you want to eat something.

Is it to help you feel less stressed out?

Is it because you are with your family and you all love having pie at Thanksgiving?

Being aware of why you are drawn to certain foods, is hugely empowering. It allows you to make the choice of what you are putting into your body, instead of feeling peer pressured or feeling like a victim to the food around you.

The choice is always yours when it comes to what you choose to put into your body. You have the power to be self-aware and you have the power to choose.

Shopping List

The shopping lists in this 30-Day Meal Plan are grouped by recipe. This is because you may not want to cook every single recipe in the meal plan. This allows you to have flexibility with the recipes you want to cook, as well as taking into consideration the ingredients that you may already have on hand.

Pantry Staples

Having a well-stocked pantry can help make cooking and meal prepping easier. Here are some of my favorite pantry staples that are so good to have on hand during the week:

- Salt and pepper
- **Mustard:** Dijon and yellow
- Soy sauce or coconut aminos
- Apple cider vinegar
- Honey
- Monkfruit sweetener
- Cocoa powder
- Vanilla extract
- Gluten-free flour
- Garlic powder
- Onion powder
- Dried oregano
- Dried basil
- Nutritional yeast

Eating Out Made Easy

Have you ever gone out to a restaurant and thought, "There's nothing healthy to eat here!" Then that turns into an all-out smorgasbord of food. You eat way too much or feel sick afterwards.

So here are some tips to make eating out easy:

Before you order, be mindful of how you feel.

- Are you feeling super hungry because you didn't eat breakfast, your blood sugar levels are super low and you're ready to eat a horse?
- Is this meal a moment to spend with your family and thus you want to indulge a little more?
- Whatever the reason is, know what it is. When you know it, you can make a positive decision instead of feeling like a victim to the restaurant choice, or an unhealthy menu.

It is OK to order a la carte or add to your meal.

- You are the customer, which means you can order your meal the way that you like it. So often, we feel like we are putting people out by asking for a simple swap on our plates, but really, if it is important to you, then it is important to the restaurant, and a good restaurant will be more than happy to make a meal the way that you like it.

Make a healthful, nourishing plate.

- Focus on filling half your plate with vegetables, add on a lean protein source and then add a whole food source of healthy fats.
- **Ideas for vegetables:** salads, grilled/roasted/steamed veggies
- **Ideas for lean proteins:** chicken breast, lean red meat, turkey breast, fish, seafood
- **Ideas for healthy fats:** avocado, nut/seeds, coconut oil, oil-based sugar free dressing

To get the maximum satiation from your meal, make sure you have on your plate:

- Protein
- Healthy fats
- Greens
- Fiber source
- Still hungry? Opt for a protein-based treat. This can be a little difficult if you haven't planned snacks or treats in advance. Opting for a protein-based treat will actually help you feel full.

Give yourself grace.

- Unless you're eating out at every meal, it is ok if you eat a bit more indulgently than normal. Eating has a huge emotional component and there is nothing wrong with that. Just remember that the next meal is your next choice to get closer to your goals.

Before we get started...

Before starting the 30-Day Meal Plan, take a minute to write down where you are starting from and where you are going.

What do I hope to achieve from this 30-Day Meal Plan?

Hint: Make these goals as specific and measurable as possible.

_____

_____

_____

_____

_____

Where I am starting from		
Current weight:		
Current measurements		
Hip circumference		
Waist circumference		
Thigh circumference: Right and left	RIGHT:	LEFT:
Bicep circumference: Right and left	RIGHT:	LEFT:
Chest measurement: Aim for the area where the bra strap usually hits, then measure around your whole chest (circumference).		

Week 1 Meal Plan
At A Glance

	Monday/ Tuesday	Wednesday/ Thursday	Friday/ Saturday	Sunday
Breakfast	Vanilla Raspberry Smoothie (V)	Chocolate Cashew Smoothie (V)	Banana Bread Protein Pancakes (V: use Chia Eggs)	Southwest Scramble (V: Black Beans)
Snack	Easy Homemade Hummus and Veggies (V)	Cherry Almond Protein Balls (V)	Roasted Red Pepper and Sundried Tomato Dip (V)	Celery and Nut/ Seed Butter (V)
Lunch	Everything Bagel Salad with Smoked Salmon (V: Chickpeas)	Chicken Banh Mi Bowls (V: Organic Tofu or Tempeh)	Spicy Avocado Tuna Salad (V: Chickpeas)	Fresh Farmers Market Salad (V: Chickpeas)
Snack	1 Green Apple and Almond Butter (V)	Shake-n-Go Trail Mix (V)	Double Chocolate Protein Balls (V)	Herbaceous Roasted Nuts (V: Omit egg)
Dinner	Chicken Fajitas with Cilantro Lime Cabbage Slaw (V: Black beans)	BBQ Chicken Stuffed Avocado (V: Pinto Beans)	Sheet Pan Sausage, Potatoes and Peppers (V: White Beans)	Sweet Chili Beef and Veggie Stir Fry (V: Organic Tofu or Tempeh)
Snack	1 cup Blueberries (V)	Easy Peach Sorbet (V)	Mint Choc Chip Smoothie Bowl (V)	Renata's Hot Chocolate (V)

(V) indicates a Vegan recipe or option for the meal.

Week 1 Grocery List

Vanilla Raspberry Smoothie

- 1 tbsp chia seeds
- ¼ cup raspberries, fresh or frozen
- 1 serving vanilla protein powder
- 1 cup spinach
- 1 tbsp healthy fats such as nut/seed butter or coconut oil
- 1-2 cups milk of choice, such as almond milk
- 1 cup ice

Snack: Easy Homemade Hummus and Veggies

- 1 can chickpeas, drained and rinsed
- 1 garlic clove
- Juice of 1 lemon
- 1 tbsp tahini
- ¼ cup extra virgin olive oil
- 1 tsp salt
- ½ tsp black pepper
- Up to ¼ cup water, optional

Everything Bagel Salad with Smoked Salmon

- 8 cups kale, finely sliced
- ¾ cup cherry tomatoes, halved
- ½ cucumber, thinly sliced
- 1 avocado, halved and cut into slices
- 4-5 radishes, thinly sliced
- 2 tbsp extra virgin olive oil
- 1 tbsp fresh lemon juice
- 1 tbsp Everything-but-the-Bagel seasoning
- 8 oz smoked salmon
- 1 cup cooked/canned chickpeas (V)

Snack: Apple and Almond Butter

- 1 medium apple
- 2 tbsp almond butter

Chicken Fajitas with Cilantro Lime Cabbage Slaw

For the Slaw:

- 4 cups cabbage, very finely sliced
- 1 cup cilantro, roughly chopped
- 1 tsp salt
- ½ tsp pepper
- ¼ cup light mayonnaise
- 1 large lime, halved

Chicken Fajita Marinade:

- ½ cup coconut aminos/soy sauce
- ½ cup lime juice
- ½ cup olive oil
- 3 cloves garlic, minced
- 2 tsp ground cumin
- 1 tbsp chili powder
- 2 tsp black pepper
- 2 lb chicken breasts

Optional additions:

- 1 cup black beans, drained and rinsed
- 1 large tomato, chopped
- ¼ cup onions, finely chopped
- 2 fresh jalapenos, sliced thinly

Snack: 1 cup of Blueberries

- 1 cup of blueberries

Chocolate Cashew Smoothie

- 1 tbsp chia seeds
- 1 serving chocolate protein powder
- 1 cup greens, such as spinach or kale
- 2 tbsp raw cashews
- 1–2 cups milk of choice, such as almond milk, or water
- 1 cup ice

Snack: Cherry Almond Protein Balls

- 1 cup raw almonds
- 1 cup raw Medjool dates, soaked in warm water for about 10 minutes, then drained
- 3 tbsp vanilla protein powder
- ½ cup dried cherries, no added sugar

Chicken Banh Mi Bowls

For the Marinade:

- 2 tbsp coconut aminos
- Juice and zest of half a lime
- 1 garlic clove, finely chopped
- ½ tsp fresh ginger, grated
- ½ tsp black pepper

For the Quick Pickled Veggies:

- ¼ cup water
- ¼ cup rice wine vinegar
- 1 tsp sesame oil
- 1 small carrot, julienned
- ½ cucumber, finely sliced
- 1 jalapeno, finely sliced

For the Dressing:

- ¼ cup light mayo
- 1 garlic clove, finely chopped
- 2 tsp rice wine vinegar
- 1 tbsp sesame oil
- ½ tsp salt
- ¼ tsp black pepper
- 1 tsp olive oil
- 1 lb chicken breast

For the Salad:

- 4 cups salad greens
- 1 handful of cilantro
- **Vegan option:** Organic, non-GMO tofu

Snack: Shake-n-Go Trail Mix

- 2½ cups raw or toasted nuts or seeds, such as roasted or natural almonds, peanuts, cashews, pumpkin seeds, sesame seeds, etc.
- 1 cup of dried fruit, no added sugars, such as dried apricots, cranberries, apple slices, dates, figs,
- Pinch salt
- ½ tsp ground cinnamon or spice of choice
- Turmeric
- Ginger
- Black pepper

BBQ Chicken Stuffed Avocado Salad

- 8 oz shredded cooked chicken breast
- 1–2 tbsp your favorite sugar-free BBQ sauce
- ½ avocado
- 1 cup salad greens
- ½ cup chopped celery
- ½ cup chopped carrots
- ½ lemon
- 1 tsp hemp hearts
- **Vegan option:** 1 cup canned kidney beans, drained and rinsed

Snack: Easy Peach Sorbet

- 2 cups frozen peaches
- ¼–½ cup water
- ¼ cup monkfruit sweetener, optional

Banana Bread Protein Pancakes

- 1 very ripe, large banana
- 2 eggs, separated
- 1 tsp ground cinnamon
- ¼ tsp ground nutmeg
- 1 tsp vanilla extract
- ⅓ cup vanilla flavored protein powder
- ¼ tsp baking powder

Optional toppings

- Chopped strawberries, blueberries, chopped walnuts or pecans.

Vegan Banana Bread Protein Pancakes

- 2 tbsp chia seeds
- 5 tbsp water
- 1 large banana, mashed
- 1 tsp ground cinnamon
- ¼ tsp ground nutmeg
- 1 tsp vanilla extract
- ⅛ tsp baking powder
- 4 tbsp vanilla flavored protein powder

Optional toppings

- Chopped strawberries, blueberries, chopped walnuts or pecans.

Snack: Roasted Red Pepper and Sundried Tomato Dip

- ½ cup roasted red peppers drained of any liquid that is in the jar
- ¼ cup sundried tomatoes, drained of any liquids
- 1 cup white beans such as cannellini beans
- 1 large garlic clove
- 3 tbsp olive oil
- Salt and pepper to taste

Spicy Avocado Tuna Salad

For the Spicy Avocado Tuna Salad:

- Two 5 oz cans of tuna in water
- ⅓ cup mashed avocado
- 1 tbsp lemon juice
- 1 jalapeno, chopped
- 1 tsp onion powder
- 1 tsp garlic powder
- ½ cup grapes, quartered
- ¼ tsp pepper
- ¼ cup lightly salted almonds roughly chopped
- **Vegan option:** 10 oz cooked or canned and drained chickpeas
- 4 cups spinach

Snack: Double Chocolate Protein Balls

- ⅔ cup gluten-free oats
- ½ cup sugar free peanut or almond butter
- 1 tbsp honey or other liquid sweetener
- ¼ cup chocolate protein powder
- 1 tbsp sugar-free chocolate chips
- 1 tbsp chia seeds

Sheet Pan Sausage, Potatoes and Peppers

- 2 tbsp olive oil
- 2 lbs turkey sausage
- 1 large onion, sliced
- 3 large bell peppers, any colors, sliced
- 3 zucchini, cut into 3" chunks
- 2 large sweet potatoes, chopped into 2" chunks
- 2 cloves garlic, minced
- 1 tbsp dried basil
- 1 tbsp dried oregano
- 1 tsp salt
- ½ tsp black pepper

Snack: Mint Chocolate Chip Smoothie Bowl

- 1 tbsp chia seeds
- 1 serving vanilla protein powder
- 1 tsp mint extract
- 1 cup greens such as kale, spinach etc.
- 1 tbsp healthy fats such as nut/seed butter or coconut oil
- 1 cups milk of choice, such as almond milk
- 1 cup ice
- 2 tbsp stevia sweetened chocolate chips

Toppings

- Fresh berries, dried unsweetened coconut, nut/seed butter.

Southwest Scramble

For the Veggies:

- 1 tbsp olive oil
- 1 medium sweet potato
- 1 onion, finely sliced
- 2 bell peppers, any color, sliced
- 4 cups greens such as kale or spinach

For the Scrambled Eggs:

- 8 eggs
- ¼ cup milk of choice
- 1 tsp salt
- ½ tsp black pepper
- 1 can black beans, drained and rinsed
- 2 avocados, diced
- Your favorite salsa
- **Optional garnish:** Chopped cilantro

Snack: Celery and Nut/Seed Butter

- 2 tbsp nut/seed butter
- Unlimited celery sticks

Fresh Farmers Market Salad

For the Lemon Dijon Dressing:

- 1 tsp dijon mustard
- 2 tsp lemon juice
- ¼ cup extra virgin olive oil
- ½ tsp salt
- ¼ tsp pepper

For the Salad:

- 4 cups salad greens
- 1 tomato, chopped into bite sized pieces
- 2 hard boiled eggs, sliced
- 2 cups sliced turkey
- ¼ cup berries, like strawberries, blackberries etc.
- 1 cup carrots, cut into matchsticks
- 1 cup sugar snap peas, chopped into bite sized pieces
- ¼ cup pickles or olives
- **Vegan option:** White beans such as cannellini beans

Snack: Herbaceous Roasted Nuts

- 1 large egg white
- ¼ tsp pink Himalayan salt
- 1½ tbsp raw agave nectar
- ¾ tsp garlic powder
- ½ tbsp dried rosemary
- ½ tbsp dried sage leaves
- ½ tbsp dried oregano
- 2 cups raw cashew nuts
- 1 cup raw almonds

Breakfast:

Vanilla Raspberry Smoothie

Servings: 1 person

Ingredients:

1 tbsp chia seeds
¼ cup raspberries, fresh or frozen
1 serving vanilla protein powder
1 cup spinach
1 tbsp healthy fats such as nut/seed butter or coconut oil
1-2 cups milk of choice, such as almond milk
1 cup ice

Instructions:

Put all ingredients into a high-speed blender.

Blend until all ingredients are well combined and there are no chunks.

Enjoy immediately!

I love starting the day with a smoothie! There are so many benefits to this.

One, smoothies are super quick and easy to make and can be an awesome option for those busy mornings when we would normally opt just to not eat.

Two, we need to start our day with a protein rich breakfast to help to stabilize our blood sugar levels, and a smoothie is a great way to do this.

Three, smoothies can be a powerhouse of nutrition. You can pack so much goodness into these smoothies that will fuel and nourish your body.

Four, there are so many ways to make smoothies! There are a multitude of delicious ingredient combinations and you'll see many of them in the smoothies during this 30-Day Meal Plan. Here is one of my favorites with vanilla and raspberries... yum!

Tip:

If using frozen raspberries, you may not need as much ice.

Look for the Good

Everyday, life can throw us curveballs. Whether it's sleeping past your alarm, your favorite shirt having a big old stain on it or missing a turn to get to work on time, these curveballs are enough to make anyone have a crappy day. But what I encourage you to do is retrain your brain to look for the good. This is the most important thing to remember about this 30-day journey.

Looking for the good in everyday helps you to give yourself grace on the days where eating healthier is a little harder, or when you get take out because you haven't meal prepped food for that day.

When you practice looking for the good, your reticular activating system, RAS, in your brain, looks for more evidence for that thought to be true. So in turn, it becomes easier for you to keep finding more good things that have happened in your day.

Set aside a couple of minutes each day to reflect and find the good things that have happened to you.

Snack

Easy Homemade Hummus & Veggies

Serving Size: 1 person

2 tbsp hummus
Unlimited veggies for dipping!

Ingredients:

1 can chickpeas, drained and rinsed
1 garlic clove
Juice of 1 lemon
1 tbsp tahini
¼ cup extra virgin olive oil
1 tsp salt
½ tsp black pepper
Up to ¼ cup water, optional

Instructions:

Add the chickpeas, garlic, lemon juice and tahini to a high-speed blender or food processor.

Turn on the blender or food processor, and blend until the ingredients are starting to get chopped up but might be getting stuck to the sides of the walls.

With the blender or food processor running, gradually pour in the olive oil to start making the hummus creamier and to allow the ingredients to start coming together and get fully blended. You may need to use a spoon or spatula to scrape down the sides of the blender or food processor container.

If you like a thinner hummus, add up to ¼ cup of water by gradually pouring it into the hummus with the blender or food processor running.

Taste and season with salt & pepper as needed.

Store in an airtight container in the fridge for up to one week.

Here is a quick and easy homemade hummus recipe that you can make ahead and keep for snacks later in the week.

Don't feel like making your own hummus? That's ok! Let the store help you. You can purchase hummus from the grocery store and even some pre-washed and chopped veggies for dipping.

Tip:

You can also portion out individual servings of hummus and vegetables into small containers for easy grab and go snacks during the week.

Lunch

Everything Bagel Salad with Smoked Salmon

Servings: 2 people

Ingredients:

8 cups kale, finely sliced
¾ cup cherry tomatoes, halved
½ cucumber, thinly sliced
1 avocado, halved and cut into slices
4–5 radishes, thinly sliced
2 tbsp extra virgin olive oil
1 tbsp fresh lemon juice
1 tbsp Everything-but-the-Bagel seasoning
8 oz smoked salmon
1 cup cooked/canned chickpeas (V)

Instructions:

Prepare salad by spreading kale across a serving platter.

Top with layers of tomatoes, cucumber, avocado and radishes.

Drizzle salad with olive oil and lemon juice and season with Everything-but-the-Bagel seasoning.

Top with smoked salmon, or chickpeas for a vegan version.

This recipe is one of the favorites with my clients. It is also a super versatile recipe. You can change the protein source to something else you may like, such as chicken, turkey or shrimp. For vegans, chickpeas or organic non-GMO tofu or tempeh can be awesome additions as well.

Tip:

If meal prepping this salad, add the avocado and dressing right before serving.

Snack

Apple and Almond Butter

Serving size: 1 person

1 medium apple
2 tbsp almond butter

L et the store help you! Easy snack ideas like apple and almond butter, are a great time saver and quick snack when your day is busy, but you still want to fuel your body.

The combination of the natural sugars from the apple, and the healthy fats and protein from the nut butter, gives you a quick burst of energy while also helping to maintain a steadier blood sugar level in the long term. That means, you have more energy for longer.

Dinner

Chicken Fajitas with Cilantro Lime Cabbage Slaw

Servings: 2 people

Ingredients:

For the Slaw:

4 cups cabbage, very finely sliced
1 cup cilantro, roughly chopped
1 tsp salt
½ tsp pepper
¼ cup light mayonnaise
1 large lime, halved

Chicken Fajita Marinade:

½ cup coconut aminos/soy sauce
½ cup lime juice
½ cup olive oil
3 cloves garlic, minced
2 tsp ground cumin
1 tbsp chili powder
2 tsp black pepper
2 lb chicken breasts

Optional additions:

1 cup black beans, drained and rinsed
1 large tomato, chopped
¼ cup onions, finely chopped
2 fresh jalapenos, sliced thinly

Instructions:

For the Chicken Fajitas:

In a large bowl or resealable bag, add the coconut aminos/soy sauce, lime juice, olive oil, garlic, cumin, chili powder and black pepper. Mix together thoroughly.

Add the chicken breasts and submerge in the marinade as much as possible.

Cover the bowl with plastic wrap or seal the bag and keep the chicken and marinade in the fridge for a minimum of 30 mins, or up to overnight.

For the Slaw:

In a large bowl, add cabbage, cilantro, mayo, salt and pepper.

Squeeze over the lime juice then toss altogether to combine thoroughly.

To cook the chicken:

Preheat the oven to 425°F or preheat the outdoor grill.

If using the oven, prepare a large baking sheet. Pick up the chicken with tongs and allow as much of the marinade to drip off of the chicken as possible, then place onto the baking sheet. Bake in a preheated oven until completely cooked through, approximately 20–30 mins depending on the thickness of chicken.

If using the grill, grill the chicken for approximately 5–10 minutes per side, depending on the thickness of the chicken.

Slice chicken into large strips.

To serve:

Place a serving of the slaw onto a serving plate. Top with chicken slices, plus any additional toppings you'd like to add. Enjoy!

Tex Mex meals are so full of flavor, which is why so many people love them. I am taking the same beloved flavor and putting a healthy twist on it!

Tip:

For the vegan version, black beans are an awesome addition because they are high in both protein and fiber. This helps to fill you up and fuel your body.

Snack

1 cup of Blueberries

Finish off the day with something sweet. Blueberries have a nice sweetness to them as well as being full of water and fiber. Feel free to use fresh or frozen and thawed blueberries.

Serving size: 1 person

1 cup blueberries

Breakfast:

Chocolate Cashew Smoothie

Cashews are one of my favorite nuts because they are so buttery. They lend themselves to this smoothie to make it extra creamy and delicious, but also, they are an awesome source of healthy fats and protein.

Servings: 1 person

Ingredients:

1 tbsp chia seeds
1 serving chocolate protein powder
1 cup greens, such as spinach or kale
2 tbsp raw cashews
1-2 cups milk of choice, such as almond milk, or water
1 cup ice

Instructions:

Put all ingredients into a high-powered blender.

Blend until all ingredients are well combined and there are no chunks.

Enjoy immediately!

Tip:

For this smoothie, a high-powered blender will ensure the cashews are perfectly blended and there is no grittiness in the smoothie. If you do not have a blender like this, you can also soak the cashews overnight in water, then drain them and add to your blender with the other smoothie ingredients. Soaking the cashews will ensure that the cashews are blended more easily.

Wednesday/Thursday

Snack

Cherry Almond Protein Balls

This is one of my favorite protein balls from the blog, NourishwithRenata.com. I have served these protein balls at a wellness retreat and people couldn't get enough of them!

Servings: 4 people

Ingredients:

1 cup raw almonds
1 cup raw Medjool dates, soaked in warm water
   for about 10 minutes, then drained
3 tbsp vanilla protein powder
½ cup dried cherries, no added sugar

Instructions:

In a food processor or high-speed blender, add in the almonds and process until roughly chopped. Almond pieces should be pea size or smaller. Pour out into a bowl.

Add the dates into the food processor or high-speed blender. Blend the dates until a ball or paste forms.

Add the chopped almonds and the protein powder into the food processor or high-speed blender. Blend until the mixture is well combined, scraping down the sides as needed. You may need to pour the mixture into a separate bowl and then knead in the protein powder into it.

Add the cherries to the mixture and knead to combine.

Take tablespoons of the mixture and roll between the palms of your hands to create a smooth surface on the protein balls. Continue making protein balls with the remaining mixture.

Chill the protein balls in the fridge for about 30 minutes in an airtight container. Enjoy cold for a firmer texture, or at room temperature for a creamier texture.

love the Vietnamese sandwich called Banh Mi. This salad takes the flavors of a Chicken Banh Mi and turns it into a hearty and delicious salad.

Wednesday/Thursday

Lunch

Chicken Banh Mi Bowls

Servings: 2 people

Ingredients:

1 tsp olive oil
1 lb chicken breast

For the Marinade:

2 tbsp coconut aminos
Juice and zest of half a lime
1 garlic clove, finely chopped
½ tsp fresh ginger, grated
½ tsp black pepper

For the Quick Pickled Veggies:

¼ cup water
¼ cup rice wine vinegar
1 tsp sesame oil
1 small carrot, julienned
½ cucumber, finely sliced
1 jalapeno, finely sliced

For the Dressing:

¼ cup light mayo
1 garlic clove, finely chopped
2 tsp rice wine vinegar
1 tbsp sesame oil
½ tsp salt
¼ tsp black pepper

For the Salad:

4 cups salad greens
1 handful of cilantro
Vegan option: Organic, non-GMO tofu

Tip:

For the vegan option, substitute non-GMO organic tofu for the chicken. You can cut it into cubes, marinate it the same way as the chicken, then pan sauté the tofu to your desired crispness.

Instructions:

In a small bowl, mix together the chicken breast and the marinade ingredients. Cover the bowl, and allow it to sit in the refrigerator, for at least 30 mins.

For the quick pickled veggies, add the water, rice wine vinegar and sesame oil to a mason jar. Put the lid on and shake well to combine. Open the jar, and add in the carrots, cucumber and jalapenos. Make sure to push the veggies underneath the pickling liquid as much as possible. Put the lid back on and transfer the jar to the fridge. Allow to sit for at least 30 mins before serving.

For the dressing, add all the ingredients to a mason jar. Put on the lid and shake vigorously to combine.

When ready to cook the chicken, heat a large pan over medium heat. Add 1 tsp olive oil. When the pan is hot, add the chicken and cook until the underside is golden brown, about 5 mins. Turn the chicken over and continue cooking for another 5 mins, or until the chicken is completely cooked through.

To serve, put 2 cups of salad greens on a plate. Top with half of the chicken, a couple of spoonfuls of the quick pickled veggies, and drizzle over the dressing. Garnish with some chopped cilantro, if desired. Enjoy!

Store any remaining ingredients in an airtight container in the fridge.

Tip:

Making food flavorful is easy! If you're looking for more flavor, think about adding spices and herbs, such as the garlic, ginger and cilantro, used in this recipe. You can also add dried spices, like cumin, turmeric, chili powder or cinnamon, to wake up your dishes and add new life to some of your favorite foods!

Variations:

Golden Trail Mix:

Nut choices: Almonds, cashews, pumpkin seeds, pistachios

Fruit choices: Dried apricots, coconut flakes, goji berries, dried ginger

Spice choices:
½ tsp ground cinnamon
½ tsp ground turmeric
⅛ tsp ground black pepper

Sweet Heat Trail Mix:

Nut choices: Cashews, almonds, sunflower seeds, pistachios

Fruit choices: dried mango, dried apricots, dried dates

Spice choices:
¼ tsp cayenne pepper
¼ tsp ancho chile pepper
¼ tsp salt
¼ tsp black pepper
¼ tsp garlic powder

Asian Inspired Trail Mix:

Nut choices: Almonds, dried edamame, dried peas, peanuts, cashews, sesame seeds

Fruit choices: Dried mango, dried orange, dried apricot, dried ginger, coconut flakes

Spice choices:
¼ tsp ginger powder
¼ tsp garlic powder
¼ tsp wasabi powder or dried chili flakes.

Snack

Shake-n-Go Trail Mix

This is a quick and easy snack that has a myriad of fun flavor combos to keep life interesting!

Servings: 4 people

Ingredients:

2½ cups raw or toasted nuts or seeds, such as roasted or natural almonds, peanuts, cashews, pumpkin seeds, sesame seeds, etc.
1 cup of dried fruit, no added sugars, such as dried apricots, cranberries, apple slices, dates, figs,
Pinch salt
½ tsp ground cinnamon or spice of choice

Instructions:

In a large resealable bag, add all of the ingredients.

Seal the bag then shake thoroughly to mix all of the ingredients.

Portion out the mixture into 4 servings placed in 4 smaller resealable bags or containers. Seal tightly and store for up to 2 weeks in a cool, dry place.

Dinner

BBQ Chicken Stuffed Avocado Salad

Servings: 1 person

Ingredients:

8 oz shredded cooked chicken breast
1-2 tbsp your favorite sugar-free BBQ sauce
½ avocado
1 cup salad greens
½ cup chopped celery
½ cup chopped carrots
½ lemon
1 tsp hemp hearts
Vegan option: 1 cup canned kidney beans, drained and rinsed

This is such an impressive looking meal, but it is so simple to make! Meal prep the BBQ chicken and keep it in a container in the fridge. Then prior to serving, halve the avocado and fill up the hole where the seed was and voila! You have a quick and easy meal. You can also easily double or triple this recipe if you're cooking for more than one person.

Instructions:

In a small bowl, mix together the chicken breast and your favorite BBQ sauce.

Take half of the avocado and scoop out a little more of the avocado flesh to make a larger opening for the BBQ chicken to sit in. You can add this scooped out avocado flesh to your salad.

Spoon the chicken into the avocado.

On a serving plate, place your salad greens, chopped celery, chopped carrots and the scooped out avocado flesh.

In the center of the plate, place the stuffed avocado.

Squeeze a little lemon juice onto the salad greens and avocado.

Sprinkle over the hemp hearts for added crunch.

Enjoy!

Tips:

To prevent the remaining half of the avocado from browning, squeeze over some lemon juice.

For the vegan option, substitute kidney beans, drained and rinsed, for the chicken.

Snack

Easy Peach Sorbet

Serving size: 2 people

Ingredients:

2 cups frozen peaches
¼–½ cup water
¼ cup monkfruit sweetener, optional

Instructions:

In a high-speed blender or food processor, add the peaches and ¼ cup water.

Blend until completely smooth. You may need to use a spatula to wipe down the sides of the blender and then resume blending.

If the blender doesn't seem to be blending very well, you can add an additional ¼ cup water to get the blender moving again. Just don't add so much water that it turns into a smoothie!

Once the sorbet is blended, taste and see if you'd like to add more sweetener. If so, add the monkfruit sweetener and blend one last time.

Serve immediately.

Finish off the day with something sweet. Peaches have a great natural sweetness and blending them creates an easy and satisfying sorbet.

Tips:

Add more flavor to this sorbet with these ideas:

Add 1 tsp vanilla extract

Chop 1 tbsp mint leaves and stir into the sorbet

Instead of water, use coconut milk for a creamier flavor and taste.

This sorbet is best made and served on the same day. You can place any leftovers in the freezer in an airtight container. However, ensure it has plenty of time to thaw before enjoying it the next time.

Breakfast

Banana Bread Protein Pancakes

These Banana Bread Protein Pancakes are not like traditional pancakes. They are made with no refined flour. Instead, I use protein powder which helps regulate blood sugar and helps us feel fuller for longer. These pancakes also cook low and slow to ensure that they cook all the way through.

Servings: 2 people

Ingredients

1 very ripe, large banana
2 eggs, separated
1 tsp ground cinnamon
¼ tsp ground nutmeg
1 tsp vanilla extract
⅓ cup vanilla flavored protein powder
¼ tsp baking powder
Optional toppings: Chopped strawberries, blueberries, chopped walnuts or pecans.

Instructions

In a medium sized bowl, add the banana and mash well.

Add the ground cinnamon, ground nutmeg, vanilla extract, vanilla-flavored protein powder and baking powder. Stir well until no clumps remain.

In a small sized bowl, separate the eggs so that the egg whites are in the new bowl, and the egg yolks go into the medium-sized bowl.

Beat the egg whites until stiff peaks form. You can do this using a handheld whisk or an electric mixer.

Tips:

To meal prep these pancakes, make the full batch and reheat the following day.

For the vegan version, see the next recipe!

Mix the egg yolks into the pancake batter in the medium-sized bowl.

Fold the beaten egg whites into the pancake batter. At first, scoop about 1/3 of the beaten egg white into the batter and mix well - don't worry about deflating the eggs at this time.

Add the second batch of the beaten egg whites and gently fold into the mixture. Repeat with the third batch of egg whites. The batter should be light and fluffy

Preheat a non-stick pan over a low to medium low heat. Spray with cooking oil spray or butter.

Spoon large tablespoons of the batter onto the heated non-stick pan.

Cook the pancakes until the underside is golden brown and the inside is cooked through. Flip the pancakes and continue to cook on the other side.

Repeat with the remaining batter.

Serve pancakes with fresh fruit such as strawberries and blueberries, and a sprinkling of chopped nuts like walnuts or pecans.

Tip:

There are so many kinds of protein powders available now, so how do you choose which one to eat? It depends on what your goals are and what your body responds to best. There are two kinds of protein powders: one sourced from whey (dairy) and the other sourced from plants, such as peas. If you don't tolerate dairy very well, you likely would opt for a plant-based protein.

Also, if you are limiting your refined sugar intake, I encourage you to read the protein powder labels, to see which protein powders have no or low refined sugars, or are sweetened with a sugar substitute, such as stevia or monkfruit sweetener.

Lastly, so many protein powders contain other ingredients, such as ground vegetable or greens powders. If you're aiming to increase your vitamin and mineral intake, you may want to opt for a protein powder with these extra ingredients included.

Vegan Banana Bread Protein Pancakes

Servings: 2 people

Ingredients:

2 tbsp chia seeds
5 tbsp water
1 large banana, mashed
1 tsp ground cinnamon
¼ tsp ground nutmeg

1 tsp vanilla extract
⅛ tsp baking powder
4 tbsp vanilla flavored protein powder
Optional toppings: chopped strawberries, blueberries, chopped walnuts or pecans.

Instructions:

In a small bowl, mix together the chia seeds and water. Allow to sit for 5 mins to become gelatinous.

In a separate medium sized bowl, add the banana, ground cinnamon, ground nutmeg, vanilla extract, baking powder and protein powder. Stir to combine.

Add the chia seed mixture to the banana mixture and stir to combine.

Heat a non-stick pan with some non-stick spray over medium low heat.

Once warm, add tablespoons of the pancake batter to the pan. Allow to cook on one side for 3-5 minutes, until a golden-brown crust has formed.

Carefully use a spatula to flip the pancakes to the other side. Allow the pancakes to develop another golden-brown crust on the other side, about 3-5 minutes.

Transfer the cooked pancakes to a separate plate to keep warm, while you cook the remaining pancake batter. This recipe makes approximately 9-10 pancakes.

Serve pancakes warm with berries and chopped nuts, if desired.

Tip:

This recipe makes softer pancakes, not like traditional pancakes. However, as they cool, they will become firmer.

Snack

Roasted Red Pepper and Sundried Tomato Dip

Tip:

Keep in an airtight container in the fridge for up to 1 week.

Servings: 4 people

Ingredients:

½ cup roasted red peppers drained of any liquid that is in the jar

¼ cup sundried tomatoes, drained of any liquids

1 cup white beans such as cannellini beans

1 large garlic clove

3 tbsp olive oil

Salt and pepper to taste

Instructions:

In a blender or food processor, add all ingredients except salt and pepper.

Blend until well combined and to the desired texture. If you want the dip to be smoother, blend it for longer. For a chunkier dip, blend until just combined.

Taste dip and add salt and pepper to taste. Blend or stir once more to incorporate the salt and pepper.

Pour into a bowl and serve with veggies, like cucumbers, celery and carrots, for dipping.

Lunch

Spicy Avocado Tuna Salad

Servings: 2 people

Ingredients:

For the Spicy Avocado Tuna Salad:

2 x 5-oz cans of tuna in water
⅓ cup mashed avocado
1 tbsp lemon juice
1 jalapeno, chopped
1 tsp onion powder
1 tsp garlic powder
½ cup grapes, quartered
¼ tsp pepper
¼ cup lightly salted almonds roughly chopped
Vegan option: 10 oz cooked or canned and drained chickpeas

4 cups spinach

Instructions:

In a medium sized bowl, add all ingredients and mix thoroughly.

For 1 serving, add 2 cups of spinach onto a large plate, top with half of the Spicy Avocado Tuna Salad. Enjoy!

Keep any leftovers in an airtight container in the fridge.

Tip:

Healthy fats are an important part of any meal. They help to slow your digestion, so you feel fuller for longer. Healthy fats come from avocados, coconut oil, olive oil, nuts and seeds. Be sure to include healthy fats in your meals so you always feel satiated!

Snack

Double Chocolate Protein Balls

Servings: 10 balls

Ingredients:

⅔ cup gluten free oats
½ cup sugar free peanut or almond butter
1 tbsp honey or other liquid sweetener

¼ cup chocolate protein powder
1 tbsp sugar-free chocolate chips
1 tbsp chia seeds

Instructions:

In a large bowl, mix the oats, peanut (or almond) butter, honey or other liquid sweetener, protein powder, chocolate chips and chia seeds until well combined.

If the mixture is too soft, you may need to add more oats. If the mixture is too dry, you may need to add a little more nut butter or liquid sweetener.

Measure a heaping tablespoon and roll it into a ball. Continue with the remaining mixture.

Keep the protein balls in the fridge for up to 1 week.

Dinner

Sheet Pan Sausage, Potatoes and Peppers

Servings: 4 people

Ingredients:

2 tbsp olive oil
2 lbs turkey sausage
1 large onion, sliced
3 large bell peppers, any colors, sliced
3 zucchini, cut into 3" chunks
2 large sweet potatoes, chopped into 2" chunks
2 cloves garlic, minced
1 tbsp dried basil
1 tbsp dried oregano
1 tsp salt
½ tsp black pepper

Instructions:

Preheat the oven to 400° F.

To a large baking sheet, add the sausage, onion, bell peppers, zucchini and sweet potato chunks.

In a small bowl, add the olive oil, garlic, dried basil, dried oregano, salt and pepper.

Drizzle the flavored olive oil over the ingredients in the tray. Toss together until all the ingredients are well coated with the flavored olive oil.

Roast the sausage and veggies in a preheated oven for approximately 20-25 mins, or until the sausages are cooked through and the veggies are tender and caramelized around the edges.

Serve immediately.

Sheet pan dinners are a real time saver! Cooking everything on one oven tray helps lessen the mess and speed up cleaning after dinner. The key to a sheet pan dinner is to chop the ingredients into a size that allows them all to cook in the same amount of time.

Tips:

You can serve this meal with a crisp green salad and a lemony vinaigrette, if desired.

For the vegan version, you can omit the sausage and simply roast the vegetables for a delicious and hearty meal.

My love of smoothie bowls knows no bounds! This Mint Chocolate Chip Smoothie Bowl is my take on Mint Chocolate Chip ice cream... but healthier! You will feel filled and fueled up with this healthy sweet treat.

Snack

Mint Chocolate Chip Smoothie Bowl

Servings: 1 person

Ingredients:

1 tbsp chia seeds
1 serving vanilla protein powder
1 tsp mint extract
1 cup greens such as kale, spinach etc.
1 tbsp healthy fats such as nut/seed butter or coconut oil
1 cups milk of choice, such as almond milk
1 cup ice
2 tbsp stevia sweetened chocolate chips
Toppings: Fresh berries, dried unsweetened coconut, nut/seed butter.

Instructions:

Put all ingredients, except the chocolate chips and toppings, into a high-speed blender.

Blend until all ingredients are well combined and there are no chunks. This smoothie should be much thicker than a drinking smoothie.

Add the chocolate chips to the smoothie and blend very quickly to break up the chocolate chips but not pulverize them.

Pour the smoothie into a bowl and top with your favorite toppings, such as fresh berries, dried unsweetened coconut, and a drizzle of nut/seed butter.

Breakfast

Southwest Scramble

Servings: 4 people

Ingredients:

For the Veggies:

1 tbsp olive oil
1 medium sweet potato
1 onion, finely sliced
2 bell peppers, any color, sliced
4 cups greens such as kale or spinach

For the Scrambled Eggs:

8 eggs
¼ cup milk of choice
1 tsp salt
½ tsp black pepper

1 can black beans, drained and rinsed
2 avocados, diced
Your favorite salsa
Optional garnish: Chopped cilantro

Instructions:

Heat a large skillet over medium heat and add olive oil.

Dice sweet potatoes into small cubes, about 1" big.

Add the sweet potatoes to the warm pan and sauté until the sweet potatoes are golden brown on all sides, about 5-10 mins.

Add the onions, peppers and greens, and sauté until softened, about 5 mins.

In a large bowl, add the eggs, milk, salt and pepper. Whisk together thoroughly.

Pour the egg mixture into the pan and using a spatula, move the eggs around the pan to create scrambled eggs.

Add in the black beans and stir gently to combine.

Transfer the scramble to a serving plate and serve with sliced avocado and salsa. Sprinkle over some chopped cilantro and enjoy.

Tips:

Any leftovers can be put into resealable containers and placed in the fridge. You could even make individual portions and keep them in the fridge for easy meals later in the week.

Snack:

Celery and Nut/Seed Butter

Servings: 1 person

Let the store help you! Easy snack ideas like celery and almond butter, are a great time saver and quick snack when your day is busy, but you still want to fuel your body.

Serving size:

2 tbsp nut/seed butter
Unlimited celery sticks

Lunch:

Fresh Farmers Market Salad

This Farmers Market Salad is inspired by some of the fresh produce that you find at local farmers markets. You can substitute any of these ingredients for what is seasonal where you live. Try to incorporate lots of beautiful colors and textures to keep the salad nutrient rich and delicious.

Servings: 2 people

Ingredients:

For the Lemon Dijon Dressing:

1 tsp Dijon mustard
2 tsp lemon juice
¼ cup extra virgin olive oil
½ tsp salt
¼ tsp pepper

4 cups salad greens
1 tomato, chopped into bite sized pieces
2 hard boiled eggs, sliced
2 cups sliced turkey
¼ cup berries, like strawberries, blackberries etc.
1 cup carrots, cut into matchsticks
1 cup sugar snap peas, chopped into bite sized pieces
¼ cup pickles or olives
Vegan option: White beans such as cannellini beans

Instructions:

For the dressing, add all ingredients into a mason jar. Shake vigorously to thoroughly combine.

Add 2 cups of salad greens to a large serving plate.

Top with half of each ingredient listed above i.e. the tomato, egg, turkey, berries, carrots, sugar snap peas, pickles or olives.

Drizzle over the dressing and enjoy!

Keep remaining ingredients in an airtight container in the fridge.

Tip:

For the vegan option, simply use white beans as your protein source.

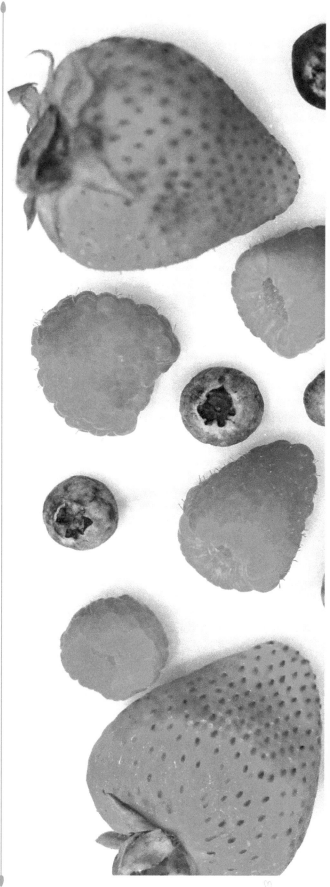

Snack:

Herbaceous Roasted Nuts

Servings: 4 people

Ingredients:

1 large egg white
½ tsp pink Himalayan salt
1½ tbsp raw agave nectar
¾ tsp garlic powder
½ tbsp dried rosemary
½ tbsp dried sage leaves
½ tbsp dried oregano
2 cups raw cashew nuts
1 cup raw almonds

Instructions:

Preheat the oven to 325° F. Spray a rimmed baking sheet with non-stick spray.

In a large bowl, whisk the egg white and salt until the mixture is foamy.

Add in the agave, garlic powder, rosemary, sage and oregano, and whisk to combine.

Add in the cashews and almonds. Gently stir until all nuts have been coated thoroughly.

Pour nut mixture on to the prepared baking sheet and spread out into an even layer.

Bake in the oven for about 15 mins then stir. Bake for another 10-15 mins until golden brown. Stir nuts as needed to prevent burning.

Allow the nuts to cool slightly before serving warm.

Store any leftovers in an airtight container, once completely cooled.

Tip:

Nuts are a great source of healthy fats and protein. But to keep them fresh and delicious, store them in an airtight container or bag in a place away from sunlight and heat. You can also store the nuts in the freezer if you don't think you'll be eating them quickly.

Dinner

Sweet Chili Beef and Veggie Stir Fry with Cauliflower Rice

Servings: 4

Ingredients:

One 10–12 oz package of cauliflower rice
1 lb ground beef
1 head broccoli, cut into florets
2 cups sliced carrots

For the Sauce:

½ cup rice wine vinegar
¼ cup monkfruit sweetener
¼ cup water
3 tsp red chili flakes, or more if you like it more spicy

Instructions:

Prepare cauliflower rice per the instructions on the packet.

In a large saucepan or wok on medium high heat, cook the ground beef until cooked through.

In a small bowl, mix together all the sauce ingredients.

Into the pan, add in the broccoli, carrots and sauce.

Stir thoroughly and cook until the sauce has coated all of the ingredients and the veggies are crisp tender.

Serve with cauliflower rice.

Save any leftovers for tomorrow's dinner!

Renata's Hot Chocolate

Servings: 1 person

Ingredients:

1½ cups milk of choice, or water, or mix of both
1 tsp cocoa powder + a dash for a topping
2 tsp stevia or monkfruit sweetener
½ tsp vanilla extract, optional

Instructions:

Heat milk and/or water in a large mug in the microwave, or in a saucepan on medium heat on the stove.

Once milk/water is warm, add in the cocoa powder, sweetener and vanilla extract, if using. Whisk together thoroughly to ensure the powders are completely dissolved in the milk/water.

Sprinkle on a dash of cocoa powder and enjoy!

Tips:

Variations:

Add ½–1 tsp of mint extract for a Mint Hot Chocolate.

Use ¾ cup of coffee and ¾ cup of milk of choice for a Mocha Hot Chocolate.

Add ½ tsp cinnamon

Week 2

It's Week 2! If you loved Week 1, you'll find more easy, healthy and delicious recipes in this week's meal plan.

This week, we are still utilizing the "Make One More" meal prep strategy. Now that you've had some experience with this strategy, how can you make it easier this week?

- **Can you get more help from the store?**
- **Can you take 5 mins each day to pre-package your snacks?**

Take a few minutes to plan ahead and plan for your healthy eating success this week!

Whatever you can do to make meal prepping a little easier for you, will help you keep it up for the long term. That is how real transformation occurs, with consistency and sustainability!

Week 2 Meal Plan
At A Glance

	Monday/ Tuesday	Wednesday/ Thursday	Friday/ Saturday	Sunday
Breakfast	Tropical Island Smoothie (V)	Cherry Limeade Smoothie (V)	Chocolate Fudge Brownie Smoothie with Pecans (V)	Poached Eggs on Sweet Potato Avocado Toast (V: No Egg)
Snack	Cranberry White Chocolate Protein Balls (V)	Sriracha Hummus and Veggies (V)	1 Green Apple and Almond Butter (V)	Celery and Nut/Seed Butter (V)
Lunch	California Turkey Cobb Salad (V: White Beans)	Spicy Sesame Zoodle Salad with Shrimp (V: Organic Tempeh)	Tuna and Quinoa Cakes (V: No Tuna)	Salmon Caesar Salad (V: Chickpeas)
Snack	1 Green Apple and Almond Butter (V)	Easy Yogurt and Fruit Parfait with Stove top Granola (V: Non-dairy yogurt)	Asian Fusion Guacamole (V)	Berries and Oranges with Nuts/Seeds and Coconut
Dinner	Thai Beef Lettuce Cups (V: Tofu)	Turkey Taco Bowls (V: Black Beans)	BBQ Burgers with Sweet Potato Salad (V: BBQ Lentils)	Chicken Piccata with Zoodles (V: beans)
Snack	1 cup Kiwifruit	1 cup Mixed Berries with Mint and Lime Zest (V)	Easy Vanilla Protein Ice Cream (V)	Mango, Ginger, Basil, Coconut Sorbet (V)

(V) indicates a Vegan recipe or option for the meal.

Week 2 Grocery List

Tropical Island Smoothie

- 1 tbsp chia seeds
- ¼ cup mango chunks
- ¼ cup pineapple chunks
- 1 serving vanilla protein powder
- 1 cup greens such as kale, spinach etc.
- 1 tbsp healthy fats such as nut/seed butter or coconut oil
- 2 cups milk of choice, such as unsweetened almond milk
- 1 cup ice

Snack: Cranberry White Chocolate Protein Balls

- ⅔ cup gluten free oats
- ½ cup sugar free peanut or almond butter
- 1 tbsp honey or other liquid sweetener
- ¼ cup vanilla protein powder
- 1 tbsp sugar-free white chocolate chips
- 1 tbsp dried cranberries
- 1 tbsp chia seeds

California Turkey Cobb Salad

For the Homemade Ranch Dressing:

- 1½ cup light mayo
- ¼ cup milk of choice
- 1½ tsp apple cider vinegar
- 3 cloves garlic, finely minced
- 2 tsp fresh dill, roughly chopped
- 1 tsp onion powder
- ½ tsp salt
- ¼ tsp pepper

For the Salad:

- 8 cups butter lettuce, roughly chopped
- 1 cup shredded carrots
- 1 cup multi-colored cherry tomatoes, sliced in half
- 2 tbsp lightly salted almonds, chopped
- 1 tbsp fresh dill, roughly chopped
- 2 soft-boiled eggs, chopped
- 1 avocado, diced
- 1 cup nitrate-free sliced turkey
- **Vegan version:** Organic non-GMO tempeh etc.

Snack: Apple and Nut/Seed Butter

- 1 medium apple
- 2 tbsp nut/seed butter

Thai Beef Lettuce Cups

- 1 lb lean ground beef
- ½ cup water chestnuts, drained
- 1 cup snow peas, roughly chopped
- 1 cup red bell peppers, finely sliced
- 2 tbsp Thai red curry paste
- ½ cup Thai basil leaves, finely sliced
- 2 tbsp roasted cashews
- 1 head butter lettuce, leaves separated
- **Vegan option:** 1 cup firm tofu per person

Snack: 1 cup of Kiwifruit

- 1 cup kiwifruit, chopped

Cherry Limeade Smoothie

- 1 tbsp chia seeds
- ½ cup cherries, fresh or frozen
- Juice of ½ lime
- 1 serving vanilla protein powder
- 1 cup greens such as kale, spinach etc.
- 1 tbsp healthy fats such as nut/seed butter or coconut oil
- 2 cups water or milk of choice, such as almond milk
- 1 cup ice

Snack: Sriracha Hummus and Veggies

- 1 can chickpeas, drained and rinsed
- 2 tbsp sriracha
- 1 garlic clove
- Juice of 1 lemon
- 1 tbsp tahini
- ¼ cup extra virgin olive oil
- 1 tsp salt
- ½ tsp black pepper
- Up to ¼ cup water, optional
- **Toppings:** Extra sriracha, if desired

Spicy Sesame Zoodle Salad with Shrimp

- 1 tsp olive oil
- 4 oz shrimp, fresh or frozen
- 1 medium zucchini
- ¼ tsp garlic powder
- ½ tsp sesame oil
- 1 tsp coconut aminos or reduced sodium soy sauce
- 1 tsp sambal oelek, or other chili sauce of choice
- ½ tsp salt
- ¼ tsp black pepper
- **Optional toppings:** Sesame seeds, cashews, or green onions
- **Vegan option:** Organic Non-GMO tempeh, sliced into bite sized pieces

Easy Yogurt and Fruit Parfait with Stovetop Granola

For the Stovetop Granola:

- 1 tbsp coconut oil
- 1 cup gluten free oats
- ½ cup sunflower seeds
- ½ cup pecan halves
- 1 tsp ground cinnamon
- Pinch salt
- 1 tsp vanilla extract
- ¼ cup chopped dried fruit e.g. dates, apricots, raisins, cranberries etc.
- ¼ cup coconut flakes

For the Parfait:

- ½ cup peaches, fresh, frozen or canned and drained
- 1 serving your favorite vanilla yogurt, low sugar preferred

Turkey Taco Bowls

- 1 tsp olive oil
- 1 lb ground turkey
- **Vegan option:** 2 cups black beans

For the Taco Seasoning:

- 1 tbsp chili powder
- 1½ tsp cumin
- 1 tsp oregano
- ½ tsp black pepper
- 1 tsp garlic powder

For the Quinoa:

- 1 cup quinoa
- 2 cups water

For the Salad Bowl:

- 1 avocado, diced
- ½ lemon
- 1 cup cherry tomatoes
- 2 cups spinach
- 1 cup canned black beans, rinsed and drained

- Your favorite salsa
- Cilantro, optional topping
- Jalapenos, optional topping

Snack: 1 cup Mixed Berries with Mint and Lime

- 1 cup mixed berries, fresh or frozen and thawed
- 1 tbsp fresh mint leaves
- ½ lime

Chocolate Fudge Brownie Smoothie with Pecans

- 1 tbsp chia seeds
- 1 serving chocolate protein powder
- 1 tbsp cocoa powder
- 2 tbsp chopped pecans, divided
- 1 cup spinach or kale
- 1-2 cups milk of choice, such as almond milk, coconut milk etc.
- 1 tbsp healthy fats such as coconut oil, nut/seed butter or ¼ of an avocado
- 1 cup ice

Snack: Apple and Nut/Seed Butter

- 1 medium green apple
- 2 tbsp nut/seed butter

Tuna and Quinoa Cakes

- 1 cup quinoa
- 2 cups water
- 2 x 5-oz cans tuna, drained
- 3 Eggs
- 1 green onion, green ends finely sliced
- 1 tsp garlic powder
- ¼ cup roasted red peppers, chopped
- ½ cup spinach, chopped
- 1 tsp salt
- ½ tsp pepper
- 1 tbsp olive oil
- **Vegan option:** ½ cup chickpeas, drained and rinsed

Snack: Asian Fusion Guacamole

- 2 large ripe avocados, seeded, peeled and coarsely chopped
- 1 medium sized tomato, chopped
- ½ cup fresh cilantro, roughly chopped
- 1-2 tbsp Asian chili sauce such as sriracha or sambal oelek (optional)
- 1 large lime, halved
- 1 tsp garlic powder
- 1 tsp ground ginger
- 1 tsp soy sauce or coconut aminos
- ½ tsp black pepper

BBQ Burgers with Sweet Potato Salad

For the Sweet Potato Salad:

- 4 large sweet potatoes, peeled and cut into bite size pieces
- 2 stalks of celery, diced

For the Dressing:

- ⅓ cup light mayonnaise (or a vegan mayo)
- 1 tbsp Dijon mustard
- 2 tsp apple cider vinegar
- 3 tbsp extra virgin olive oil
- ¾ tsp garlic powder
- ½ tsp salt
- ¼ tsp ground black pepper

BBQ Burgers with a Quick Green Salad

- 1 lb ground beef
- 2 tbsp sugar free BBQ sauce
- 2 tsp dried oregano
- 1 tsp salt
- ½ tsp black pepper
- 8 cups mixed salad greens
- ½ red onion, sliced thinly
- ½ cup cherry tomatoes, halved
- **Vegan option:** 2 cups lentils, cooked

Snack: Easy Vanilla Protein Ice Cream

- 1 can full-fat coconut milk
- 1 scoop vanilla flavored protein powder
- 2 tbsp stevia or sweetener of choice
- 1 tsp vanilla extract

Poached Eggs on Sweet Potato Avocado Toast

- 1 large sweet potato
- 1 tbsp olive oil

For the Quick Pickled Red Onions and Cucumbers:

- ½ cup cucumber, thinly sliced
- ½ red onion, thinly sliced
- 1 tsp capers
- Juice from ½ lemon
- ½ tsp salt
- ¼ tsp black pepper

For the Mashed Avocado:

- ½ avocado, mashed
- 1 tsp salt
- ½ tsp black pepper
- Juice from half a lemon

- 2 eggs
- 1 cup greens such as arugula, baby spinach, baby kale etc.

Snack: Celery and Nut/Seed Butter

- 2 tbsp nut/seed butter
- Unlimited celery sticks

Salmon Caesar Salad

- 1 tsp olive oil
- 2 x 8-oz salmon fillets
- 1 tsp salt
- ½ tsp black pepper
- 1 large head of romaine lettuce
- **Optional toppings:** Pumpkin seeds, chopped almonds

For the Dressing:

- ½ cup extra virgin olive oil
- 1 large clove garlic, peeled and finely minced
- 3 tbsp lemon juice
- 1 tsp Dijon mustard
- ½ tsp Worcestershire sauce
- Salt and pepper to taste

Snack: Berries and Oranges with Nuts/Seeds and Coconut

- ½ cup mixed berries, fresh or frozen and thawed
- 1 mandarin orange, peeled and segmented
- 2 tbsp Greek yogurt or non-dairy yogurt alternative mixed with 1 tbsp protein powder
- 1 tbsp chopped nuts of choice, such as chopped walnuts, pecans, cashews etc.
- 1 tbsp hemp hearts
- 1 tsp dried coconut flakes
- Dash of cinnamon

Chicken Piccata with Zoodles

- 1 tbsp olive oil
- 1 lb thinly sliced chicken breasts
- 1 tsp salt
- ½ tsp pepper
- 1 lemon, juiced
- 2 tbsp capers
- ½ cup artichokes, drained
- ½ cup sundried tomatoes
- 1 cup chicken stock
- 1 cup spinach, chopped
- Zoodles
- **Vegan option:** 2 cups chickpeas

Snack: Mango, Ginger and Basil Coconut Sorbet

- 1 large mango, peeled and chopped into chunks
- 1 cup coconut milk
- 2 tbsp monkfruit sweetener
- 2 tsp fresh ginger, grated finely
- ¼ cup fresh basil leaves, roughly torn with your hands.

Breakfast

Tropical Island Smoothie

Servings: 1 person

Ingredients:

1 tbsp chia seeds
¼ cup mango chunks
¼ cup pineapple chunks
1 serving vanilla protein powder
1 cup greens such as kale, spinach etc.
1 tbsp healthy fats such as nut/seed butter or
   coconut oil
2 cups milk of choice, such as unsweetened
   almond milk
1 cup ice

Instructions:

Put all ingredients into a high-speed blender.

Blend until all ingredients are well combined
and there are no chunks.

Enjoy immediately!

This smoothie tastes like a tropical island vacation! It combines two of my favorite tropical fruits, mango and pineapple, to give that delicious summery flavor to this green smoothie.

Tips:

To meal prep a smoothie, place the ingredients for the smoothie (except the milk and ice) into a small ziploc bag and place in the fridge or freezer.

Use greens powder and/or fiber powder in the smoothie for added nutritional benefits.

Snack

Cranberry White Chocolate Protein Balls

Servings: 10 people

Ingredients:

⅔ cup gluten-free oats
½ cup sugar free peanut or almond butter
1 tbsp honey or other liquid sweetener
¼ cup vanilla protein powder
1 tbsp sugar-free white chocolate chips
1 tbsp dried cranberries
1 tbsp chia seeds

Instructions:

In a large bowl, mix the oats, peanut (or almond) butter, honey or other liquid sweetener, protein powder, white chocolate chips, dried cranberries and chia seeds until well combined.

If the mixture is too soft, you may need to add more oats. If the mixture is too dry, you may need to add a little more nut butter or liquid sweetener.

Measure a heaping tablespoon and roll it into a ball. Continue with the remaining mixture.

Keep the protein balls in the fridge for up to 1 week.

Lunch

California Turkey Cobb Salad

Servings: 2 people

Ingredients:

For the Homemade Ranch Dressing:

1½ cup light mayo
¼ cup milk of choice
1½ tsp apple cider vinegar
3 cloves garlic, finely minced
2 tsp fresh dill, roughly chopped
1 tsp onion powder
½ tsp salt
¼ tsp pepper

For the Salad:

8 cups butter lettuce, roughly chopped
1 cup shredded carrots
1 cup multi-colored cherry tomatoes, sliced in half
2 tbsp lightly salted almonds, chopped
1 tbsp fresh dill, roughly chopped
2 soft-boiled eggs, chopped
1 avocado, diced
1 cup nitrate-free sliced turkey
Vegan version: Organic non-GMO tempeh etc.

Instructions:

For the dressing, add all the ingredients into a small bowl. Whisk together until fully combined. Reserve the dressing while you make the salad.

For the salad, add a layer of lettuce onto a large serving plate. Top with a layer of carrots and halved cherry tomatoes. Sprinkle over the chopped almonds and dill.

Arrange the eggs, avocado and turkey on top of the salad. Drizzle over a few tablespoons of the Ranch Dressing and serve.

Cobb Salad gets a West Coast vibe with a simple swap to more California-style ingredients.

Tip:

Store the remaining Ranch Dressing in a resealable container in the fridge for up to 1 week.

Snack

Apple and Nut/ Seed Butter

Let the store help you! Easy snack ideas like apple and almond butter, are a great time saver and quick snack when your day is busy, but you still want to fuel your body.

Serving size: 1 person

1 medium apple
2 tbsp nut/seed butter

Tip:

For the vegan option, substitute firm tofu, crumbled up into small pieces, instead of the beef.

Dinner

Thai Beef Lettuce Cups

Servings: 2 people

Ingredients:

1 lb lean ground beef
½ cup water chestnuts, drained
1 cup snow peas, roughly chopped
1 cup red bell peppers, finely sliced
2 tbsp Thai red curry paste
½ cup Thai basil leaves, finely sliced
2 tbsp roasted cashews
1 head butter lettuce, leaves separated
Vegan option: 1 cup firm tofu per person

Instructions:

Heat a large skillet over medium high heat.

Add the beef and sauté until completely cooked through.

Add the water chestnuts, snow peas and sliced red bell peppers, and toss to combine.

Add the Thai red curry paste and stir to warm the paste and allow it to coat all of the ingredients. Allow to sauté for 2-3 minutes until the veggies are crisp tender.

To make the lettuce cups, take a large lettuce leaf, and fill with a couple of spoonfuls of the red curry beef mixture. Top with a sprinkling of the Thai basil and a few roasted cashews. Enjoy!

Store any remaining filling in an airtight container in the fridge.

Snack

1 cup of Kiwifruit

Finish off the day with something sweet. Kiwifruit are high in Vitamin C, fiber and antioxidants. They also have a sweet and slightly tart flavor which keeps the taste buds guessing.

Serving size: 1 person

1 cup kiwifruit, chopped

Breakfast

Cherry Limeade Smoothie

Servings: 1 person

Ingredients:

1 tbsp chia seeds
½ cup cherries, fresh or frozen
Juice of ½ lime
1 serving vanilla protein powder
1 cup greens such as kale, spinach etc.
1 tbsp healthy fats such as nut/seed butter
   or coconut oil
2 cups water or milk of choice, such as almond
   milk
1 cup ice

Instructions:

Put all ingredients into a high-speed blender.

Blend until all ingredients and well combined and there are no chunks.

Enjoy immediately!

Tips:

To meal prep a smoothie, place the ingredients for the smoothie (except the milk and ice) into a small ziploc bag and place in the fridge or freezer.

Use greens powder and/or fiber powder in the smoothie for added nutritional benefits.

Snack

Sriracha Hummus and Veggies

This is a spicy twist on the Easy Homemade Hummus in Week 1's meal plan.

Servings: 1 person

Serving Size:

2 tbsp hummus
Unlimited veggies for dipping!

Ingredients:

1 can chickpeas, drained and rinsed
2 tbsp sriracha
1 garlic clove
Juice of 1 lemon
1 tbsp tahini

¼ cup extra virgin olive oil
1 tsp salt
½ tsp black pepper
Up to ¼ cup water, optional
Toppings: Extra sriracha, if desired

Instructions:

Add the chickpeas, sriracha, garlic, lemon juice and tahini to a high-speed blender or food processor.

Turn on the blender or food processor, and blend until the ingredients are starting to get chopped up but might be getting stuck to the sides of the walls.

With the blender or food processor running, gradually pour in the olive oil to start making the hummus creamier and to allow the ingredients to start coming together and getting fully blended. You may need to use a spoon or spatula to scrape down the sides of the blender or food processor container.

If you like a thinner hummus, add up to ¼ cup of water, by gradually pouring it into the hummus with the blender or food processor running.

Taste and season with salt and pepper as needed.

Store in an airtight container in the fridge for up to one week. You can also top with an extra drizzle of sriracha, if desired.

Tips:

To make life easier, portion out individual servings of hummus and vegetables into small containers to store in the fridge for snacks later in the week.

Lunch

Spicy Sesame Zoodle Salad with Shrimp

Servings: 1 person

Ingredients:

1 tsp olive oil
4 oz shrimp, fresh or frozen
1 medium zucchini
¼ tsp garlic powder
½ tsp sesame oil
1 tsp coconut aminos or reduced sodium soy sauce
1 tsp sambal oelek, or other chili sauce of choice
½ tsp salt
¼ tsp black pepper
Optional toppings: Sesame seeds, cashews, or green onions
Vegan option: Organic Non-GMO tempeh, sliced into bite sized pieces

Instructions:

Heat 1 tsp olive oil in a sauté pan on medium high heat.

Once hot, add the shrimp and sauté until no longer transparent. The shrimp should be pink all over.

Season with salt and black pepper. Mix well. Take off the heat while you make the salad.

Spiralize the zucchini and set aside. If you don't have a spiralizer, just use a vegetable peeler to shave long thick strands off of the sides of the zucchini until you reach the core. Then repeat on all sides. Set aside.

In a medium sized bowl, mix together the garlic powder, sesame oil, coconut aminos, soy sauce, and sambal oelek or chili sauce of choice, to make the dressing.

Add in the zucchini and toss together thoroughly with the dressing.

Place zoodles on a serving plate, top with cooked shrimp and optional toppings, like sesame seeds, cashews and/or green onions.

Enjoy!

Tip:

For the vegan version, use organic tempeh. You can slice organic tempeh into slices and quickly pan sauté in a little olive oil until it is golden brown.

Snack

Easy Yogurt and Fruit Parfait with Stovetop Granola

Servings: 1 person

Ingredients:

For the Stovetop Granola:

1 tbsp coconut oil
1 cup gluten free oats
½ cup sunflower seeds
½ cup pecan halves
1 tsp ground cinnamon
Pinch salt
1 tsp vanilla extract

¼ cup chopped dried fruit e.g. dates, apricots, raisins, cranberries etc.
¼ cup coconut flakes

For the Parfait:

½ cup peaches, fresh, frozen or canned and drained
1 serving your favorite vanilla yogurt, low sugar preferred

Instructions:

For the stovetop granola, heat coconut oil in a medium sized saucepan over medium low heat. Add oats, seeds, nuts and toss together until well combined. Add cinnamon, salt and mix until evenly distributed throughout the mixture. Add vanilla extract and stir again.

Toast granola over medium heat until golden brown, about 10 mins

Once golden, add in dried fruit, coconut and mix once more. Allow to cool before storing in an airtight container or eating.

To assemble the parfait, add half the peaches into a small bowl. Top with half the yogurt and scatter over about 1 tbsp of the cooled Stovetop Granola. Repeat the layers by adding half the peaches, then top with the remaining yogurt and another tablespoon of the granola.

Enjoy immediately!

Tips:

Store granola in an airtight container for up to 2 weeks.

To meal prep the parfaits, layer the peaches and yogurt in a resealable container or mason jar. Portion the granola into another resealable container to add to the parfait just before serving.

Dinner

Turkey Taco Bowls

Servings: 4 people

Ingredients:

1 tsp olive oil
1 lb ground turkey
Vegan option: 2 cups black beans

For the Taco Seasoning:

1 tbsp chili powder
1½ tsp cumin
1 tsp oregano
½ tsp black pepper
1 tsp garlic powder

For the Quinoa:

1 cup quinoa
2 cups water

For the Salad Bowl:

1 avocado, diced
½ lemon
1 cup cherry tomatoes
2 cups spinach
1 cup canned black beans, rinsed and drained.

Your favorite salsa
Optional toppings: Chopped cilantro, sliced
  jalapenos

Tip:

To prevent browning, you may
want to squeeze 1 tsp lemon
juice over the avocado.

For the turkey taco meat: Heat 1 tsp olive oil in a large sauté pan over medium heat.

Once the pan is hot, add the ground turkey and cook until completely cooked through. If making the vegan version, substitute the black beans instead of the turkey.

Add in the taco seasonings. Mix very well together.

For the quinoa: In a saucepan, add the quinoa and water. Stir well.

Place the saucepan on medium high heat, covered, and bring to the boil. Once it boils, reduce the heat to simmer and cook until all the water is absorbed, about 10 mins.

To make the turkey taco bowls, add 1 cup spinach into a bowl, top with ½ cup cooked quinoa, ¼ of the cooked, ground turkey, ½ cup cherry tomatoes, ½ cup black beans, ½ avocado, then top with your favorite salsa and any optional toppings such as cilantro and jalapenos.

Cool the remaining ground turkey, then store in the fridge for another meal. Alternatively, you can opt to make some more turkey taco bowls in resealable containers (using the previous step as a guide) and keep them in the fridge for future meals.

Wednesday/Thursday

Snack

1 cup Mixed Berries with Mint and Lime

Simple additions to fruit can really wake up the flavors, like adding lime juice and fresh mint leaves to beautiful berries.

Servings: 1 person

Ingredients:

1 cup mixed berries, fresh or frozen and thawed
1 tbsp fresh mint leaves
½ lime

Instructions:

To a bowl, add the mixed berries.

Tear the mint leaves with your hands and scatter over the berries.

Take the lime and squeeze the lime juice over the berries and mint.

Enjoy immediately!

To meal prep a smoothie, place
the ingredients for the smoothie
(except the milk and ice) into a
small ziploc bag and place in the
fridge or freezer.

Use greens powder and/or fiber
powder in the smoothie for
added nutritional benefits.

Friday/Saturday

Breakfast

Chocolate Fudge Brownie Smoothie with Pecans

Servings: 1 person

Ingredients:

1 tbsp chia seeds
1 serving chocolate protein powder
1 tbsp cocoa powder
2 tbsp chopped pecans, divided
1 cup spinach or kale
1-2 cups milk of choice, such as almond milk,
coconut milk etc.
1 tbsp healthy fats, such as coconut oil, nut/
seed butter or ¼ of an avocado
1 cup ice

Instructions:

Put all ingredients, except for 1 tbsp pecans, into a high-speed blender.

Blend until all ingredients and well combined and there are no chunks.

Pour into a glass and top with remaining 1 tbsp pecans.

Enjoy immediately!

Friday/Saturday

Snack

Apple and Nut/Seed Butter

Let the store help you! Easy snack ideas, like a sliced apple and your favorite nut/seed butter, are a great time saver and quick snack when your day is busy, but you still want to fuel your body.

Serving size:

1 medium green apple
2 tbsp nut/seed butter

Lunch

Tuna and Quinoa Cakes

Servings: 2 people

Ingredients:

1 cup quinoa
2 cups water
2 x 5-oz cans tuna, drained
3 eggs
1 green onion, green ends finely sliced
1 tsp garlic powder
¼ cup roasted red peppers, chopped
½ cup spinach, chopped
1 tsp salt
½ tsp pepper
1 tbsp olive oil
Vegan option: ½ cup chickpeas, drained and rinsed

Tip:

For the vegan option, omit the eggs and tuna, and simply turn this recipe into a hearty quinoa bowl. Here's how you can do this:

In a bowl, add the quinoa, olive oil, salt, pepper and garlic powder. Toss together to thoroughly coat.

Top the quinoa with spinach, roasted red peppers, and green onions. For added protein and fiber, add the chickpeas.

Enjoy!

Instructions:

To a medium sized pot, add the quinoa and water. Place the pot over medium high heat, and cover. Bring to a boil, then reduce to a simmer. Cook until all the water has been absorbed by the quinoa, about 10 mins. Allow to cool.

Meanwhile, in a large bowl, add the drained tuna, cooled quinoa, eggs, green onion, garlic powder, chopped roasted red peppers and chopped spinach. Mix together with a wooden spoon until well combined.

Heat a large skillet over medium heat. Add the olive oil.

Take large tablespoons of the quinoa and tuna mixture, form into patties, and gently fry in the hot skillet until golden brown. Carefully turn over and cook until the other side is golden brown too.

Transfer the pan-fried tuna and quinoa cakes to a baking tray and keep the tray in a warm oven.

Repeat the previous two steps with the remaining mixture.

Serve the tuna and quinoa cakes with a simple green salad and your favorite vinaigrette.

Snack

Asian Fusion Guacamole

This is a fun way to add more flavor to traditional guacamole. Just a few Asian ingredients can transform guacamole into something new and exciting!

Servings: 4 people

Ingredients:

2 large ripe avocados, seeded, peeled and coarsely chopped
1 medium sized tomato, chopped
½ cup fresh cilantro, roughly chopped
1-2 tbsp Asian chili sauce such as sriracha or sambal oelek (optional)
1 large lime, halved
1 tsp garlic powder
1 tsp ground ginger
1 tsp soy sauce or coconut aminos
½ tsp black pepper

Instructions:

Add the avocado chunks into a medium sized bowl. Using a fork or potato masher, mash the avocado to desired consistency for the guacamole.

Add the chopped tomato, cilantro, 1 tbsp of Asian chili sauce, the juice of one half of the lime, garlic powder, ginger, soy sauce/coconut aminos and pepper. Stir well to combine.

Taste the guacamole to determine if you need more lime juice, chili sauce, soy sauce/coconut aminos and/or pepper.

Serve this Asian fusion guacamole with sliced veggies, like cucumber, celery, carrot sticks or even some baked wonton chips.

Dinner

BBQ Burgers with Sweet Potato Salad

This is one of the first burger recipes I made for my husband. It is such a flavorful burger that can be paired with a salad for a feel-good take on a traditional burger. This Sweet Potato Salad is also a major crowd pleaser. I've had people request that I bring this salad to backyard BBQs since it is such a great, delicious spin on the traditional potato salad.

Servings: 4 people

Sweet Potato Salad

Ingredients:

4 large sweet potatoes, peeled and cut into bite size pieces
2 stalks of celery, diced

Dressing:

⅓ cup light mayonnaise (or a vegan mayo)
1 tbsp Dijon mustard
2 tsp apple cider vinegar
3 tbsp extra virgin olive oil
¾ tsp garlic powder
½ tsp salt
¼ tsp ground black pepper

Tip:

For the vegan version, you can use canned or homemade lentils. Once cooked per the packet instructions, mix in about ½ cup sugar free bbq sauce for some tasty flavor. Serve with the same salad as above.

Steam sweet potatoes until just tender, about 8 minutes. Try not to overcook them as the potatoes will get mushy. Allow to cool completely.

For the dressing, mix all ingredients together thoroughly. Taste and season as desired.

In a large bowl, toss together the cooled sweet potatoes, diced celery and dressing until thoroughly mixed.

Can be stored in the fridge in an airtight container for up to 1 week.

BBQ Burgers with a Quick Green Salad

Ingredients:

1 lb ground beef
2 tbsp sugar free BBQ sauce
2 tsp dried oregano
1 tsp salt
½ tsp black pepper
8 cups mixed salad greens
½ red onion, sliced thinly
½ cup cherry tomatoes, halved
Vegan option: 2 cups lentils, cooked

Instructions:

In a large bowl, add the ground beef, BBQ sauce, oregano, salt and pepper.

Mix all together using your hands.

Form 4 patties from the mixture.

Preheat the grill or heat a large nonstick skillet over medium heat on the stove top.

Add the burgers to the preheated grill or skillet. Allow to cook on one side until a good crust has formed, about 5 mins.

Carefully flip the burger patties over and cook on the other side until the burgers are cooked through.

Serve the burgers immediately over a bed of mixed salad greens, sliced onions and cherry tomatoes, with extra BBQ sauce, if desired.

Snack

Easy Vanilla Protein Ice Cream

Servings: 4 people

Ingredients:

1 can full-fat coconut milk
1 scoop vanilla flavored protein powder
2 tbsp stevia or sweetener of choice
1 tsp vanilla extract

Instructions:

In a blender, add all ingredients and blend until thoroughly combined.

Pour into an ice cream maker and allow to churn per the manufacturer's instructions.

After churning the ice cream in the ice cream maker, if a firmer consistency of ice cream is desired, transfer the ice cream to a freezer-safe container and place in the freezer for 1-2 hours.

Tips:

This ice cream is best served soon after making it. If you have set the ice cream in the freezer for too long, allow to thaw slightly at room temperature until at the desired softness.

If you don't have an ice cream maker, you can also freeze the coconut milk in an ice cube tray. Then release the coconut milk ice cubes, pop them in the blender, add the other ingredients, plus about ¼ cup water or milk of choice, and blend very well to get a soft serve consistency.

Instructions for Sides:

Preheat the oven to 420° F.

Carefully slice the sweet potato to get long "toast" shapes, approximately ½" thick.

Place sweet potato slices on a baking sheet, and drizzle over olive oil. Rub olive oil over the sweet potato slices.

Bake the sweet potato slices in a hot oven for approximately 15 mins.

Turn the sweet potato slices over, then roast for another 5-10 mins, until the sweet potato is cooked through and golden brown on the edges.

For the Quick Pickled Red Onions and Cucumbers, combine the cucumbers, red onions, capers, lemon juice, salt and pepper in a small bowl. Mix well and allow to sit for about 10 minutes while you make the rest of the recipe.

For the Mashed Avocado, add the avocado, salt, pepper and lemon juice to a small bowl. Mash all together with a fork. Set to the side.

Sunday

Breakfast

Poached Eggs on Sweet Potato Avocado Toast

Servings: 1 person

Ingredients:

1 large sweet potato
1 tbsp olive oil

For the Quick Pickled Red Onions and Cucumbers:

½ cup cucumber, thinly sliced
½ red onion, thinly sliced
1 tsp capers
Juice from ½ lemon
½ tsp salt
¼ tsp black pepper

For the Mashed Avocado:

½ avocado, mashed
1 tsp salt
½ tsp black pepper
Juice from half a lemon

2 eggs
1 cup greens such as arugula, baby spinach, baby kale etc.

Instructions for Eggs:

To poach your eggs, take a small sauté pan and fill it with water about 1" deep. Heat the sauté pan over medium low heat until the water is just barely simmering.

Crack an egg into a small bowl, to ensure no shell ends up in your poached egg.

Using a slotted spoon, slowly stir the water to create a little vortex in the water. This will help the poached egg to stay together in the water.

As the water continues to spin in the pan, carefully pour the egg into the middle of the vortex. You'll notice the egg slowly stop spinning in the water.

Continue to cook the egg until the egg white is cooked through and the egg yolk is partially cooked through, but still runny inside.

Use the slotted spoon to carefully remove the egg from the pan and place on a folded kitchen towel to help absorb any remaining water.

Repeat this process to poach the remaining egg.

To assemble, take 2 slices of sweet potato "toast" and place on a plate. Top each sweet potato "toast" with 1 heaping tablespoon of mashed avocado, a spoonful of the quick pickled cucumbers and red onions, ½ cup of greens and finally, the poached eggs!

Enjoy!

Snack

Celery and Nut/Seed Butter

Servings: 1

This is one of my favorite easy snacks. I love the crunchy celery sticks with the creaminess of the nut/seed butter. Plus, you get fiber, vitamins, minerals, healthy fats and protein from this snack too.

Serving size:

2 tbsp nut/seed butter
Unlimited celery sticks

Tip:

Meal prep your celery sticks by chopping the celery and placing it in a resealable container. Fill the container with enough water to cover the celery sticks to ensure they stay hydrated.

Instructions:

Heat a large non-stick pan on a medium heat with 1 tsp olive oil.

Season the salmon filets with salt and pepper on both sides and add to the hot pan. Cook until the underside is golden brown, about 5 mins.

Carefully flip the salmon and allow the other side to cook until golden brown, about 5 mins.

While the salmon is cooking, cut the romaine lettuce into bite size pieces.

For the dressing, add all ingredients into a mason jar and screw the lid on tight.

Vigorously shake the jar until all of the ingredients are thoroughly combined. (This is also a great arm workout!)

To serve, take half the romaine lettuce and place on a serving plate. Top with a cooked salmon filet, and drizzle over 1-2 tbsp of the dressing. Scatter over your choice of any additional toppings, like the pumpkin seeds or chopped almonds. Enjoy immediately!

Tip:

Feel free to add more veggies or even some chickpeas to this salad for extra protein, vitamins and minerals.

Sunday

Lunch

Salmon Caesar Salad

Servings: 2 people

Ingredients:

1 tsp olive oil
Two 8 oz salmon filets
1 tsp salt
½ tsp black pepper
1 large head of romaine lettuce
Optional toppings: Pumpkin seeds, chopped almonds

For the dressing:

½ cup extra virgin olive oil
1 large clove garlic, peeled and finely minced
3 tbsp lemon juice
1 tsp Dijon mustard
½ tsp Worcestershire sauce
Salt and pepper to taste

Snack

Berries and Oranges with Nuts/Seeds and Coconut

Servings: 1 person

Ingredients:

½ cup mixed berries, fresh or frozen and thawed
1 mandarin orange, peeled and segmented
2 tbsp Greek yogurt or non-dairy yogurt alternative mixed with 1 tbsp protein powder
1 tbsp chopped nuts of choice, such as chopped walnuts, pecans, cashews etc.
1 tbsp hemp hearts
1 tsp dried coconut flakes
Dash of cinnamon

Instructions:

To a bowl, add the mixed berries and mandarin orange segments.

Top with your yogurt of choice.

Scatter over the chopped nuts, hemp hearts, coconut flakes, and a dash of cinnamon.

Enjoy immediately!

Instructions:

Heat 1 tbsp olive oil in a large pan over medium-high heat.

Season the chicken with salt and pepper on both sides.

When the pan is hot, add the chicken and allow to cook until the underside is golden brown.

Using tongs, turn the chicken over and cook until browned on the second side.

You may have to cook the chicken in batches, if the pan is too small to fit all the chicken.

Remove the chicken from the pan.

Add the lemon juice, capers, artichokes, sun-dried tomatoes, chicken stock and spinach to the pan and stir to combine.

Bring the mixture to a boil, and the chicken breasts back into the pan. Reduce the heat to low and simmer until the chicken is cooked through.

Add zoodles to the hot pan and stir for approximately one minute to soften the noodles.

To serve, add noodles to a serving plate, then top with the chicken breast and as much sauce and veggies as you like.

Store the remaining food in an airtight container in the fridge for up to one week.

Sunday

Dinner

Chicken Piccata with Zoodles

Servings: 2 people

Ingredients:

1 tbsp olive oil
1 lb thinly sliced chicken breasts
1 tsp salt
½ tsp pepper
1 lemon, juiced
2 tbsp capers
½ cup artichokes, drained
½ cup sundried tomatoes
1 cup chicken stock
1 cup spinach, chopped
Zoodles
Vegan option: 2 cups chickpeas

Tip:

Try to cook the zoodles right before you plan to eat it. They can get soggy if left to sit in the sauce.

For the vegan option, simply simmer chickpeas in the lemon sauce with vegetable stock instead of chicken stock, capers, artichokes and sundried tomatoes.

Mango, Ginger and Basil Coconut Sorbet

Servings: 2 people

Ingredients:

1 large mango, peeled & chopped into chunks

1 cup coconut milk

2 tbsp monkfruit sweetener

2 tsp fresh ginger, grated finely

¼ cup fresh basil leaves, roughly torn with your hands.

Instructions:

Add the mango, coconut milk, monkfruit sweetener and ginger to a high-speed blender or food processor. Blend until completely smooth and creamy.

Transfer the sorbet into a resealable container, flatten the top surface of the sorbet, and place in the freezer.

Stir the sorbet every 30 mins to an hour until it becomes thick in texture like a soft serve ice cream.

To serve, scoop spoonfuls of the sorbet into a small bowl and scatter over the fresh basil leaves. Enjoy immediately!

Week 3

Woohoo! It's Week 3! You are officially halfway through this month. Take a few moments to reflect on these questions:

- How are you feeling?
- Do you find yourself naturally leaning towards eating healthier foods?
- How is your digestion?
- Write down how this process is going for you.
- What are you liking? What are you disliking?
- What have you learned about yourself so far?

How can you make this way of eating more sustainable, more enjoyable, more life-affirming this week?

Take some time to journal around these questions.

Remember to reach out to me if you have any questions or comments. I'd love to hear from you on social media at:

Instagram: **@nourish_with_renata**

Facebook: **www.facebook.com/getnourishedwithrenata**

Tip: Celebrate the Non-Scale Victories!

When we really want to lose weight, we tend to focus on the scale as the only measure of success. But the truth is, there are many ways to measure success in your health journey. I like to call these Non-Scale Victories. Every time you feel your jeans fitting looser, you have more energy during the day, or you're sleeping better than ever, these are all fantastic successes! Remember to celebrate them! They are all markers that you are well on your way to achieving your wellness goals.

Week 3 Meal Plan
At A Glance

	Monday/ Tuesday	Wednesday/ Thursday	Friday/ Saturday	Sunday
Breakfast	All-The-Greens Smoothie (V)	Jaffa Smoothie (V)	Blueberry Pie Smoothie (V)	Roasted Veg Souffle (V: No eggs)
Snack	Hummus and Veggies (V)	½ Apple, 1 serving Almonds	2 Mandarins, 1 serving Almonds	Celery and Nut/Seed Butter (V)
Lunch	Asian Slaw with Edamame and Orange (V)	Kale, Cashew & Basil Pesto with Chicken, Zoodles, and Sundried Tomatoes (V: White Beans)	Gado-Gado with Peanut Sauce and Chicken (V: Tofu)	Shrimp with Avocado, Cucumber, Tomato Salad (V: White Beans)
Snack	1 Banana and Nut/Seed Butter (V)	Celery and Nut/ Seed Butter (V)	Chocolate Protein Muffins (V)	1 cup Peaches, 1 serving Almonds
Dinner	Fish Taco Salad with Spicy Tomatillo Salsa (V: Black Beans)	Sesame Beef Nourish Bowls (V: Tempeh and Veggies)	BBQ Chicken Flatbread (V: Chickpeas)	Lemon Oregano Chicken and Quinoa (V: Chickpeas)
Snack	1 serving Almonds	Sugar-Free Coconut Yogurt mixed with Protein Powder (V)	Cookies & Cream Protein Ice Cream (V)	Golden Apple Crumble (V)

(V) indicates a Vegan recipe or option for the meal.

Week 3 Grocery List

All-the-Greens Smoothie

- 1 tbsp chia seeds
- 1 serving vanilla protein powder
- ½ cup chopped green apple
- 1 cup spinach or kale
- 1 stalk celery, chopped
- 1 cup cucumber, chopped
- Juice from half a lemon
- 1 tbsp coconut oil
- 1 tsp spirulina, optional
- 1-2 cups milk of choice, such as almond milk, coconut milk etc. or water
- 1 cup ice

Snack: Hummus and Veggies

- 2 tbsp hummus
- Unlimited veggies for dipping!

Asian Slaw with Edamame and Orange

- 1 tsp olive oil
- 2 lbs chicken breast
- 2 tsp salt
- 1 tsp black pepper
- For the Asian Slaw:
- 4 cups cabbage, finely sliced
- 3 carrots, cut into fine matchsticks
- ½ cup cilantro, chopped
- ½ cup edamame beans
- 2 mandarin oranges, segmented
- **Optional toppings:** Sliced almonds, sesame seeds, sliced green onions

For the Asian Slaw Dressing:

- 1 tbsp sesame oil
- 1 tsp soy sauce
- Juice of 1 lime
- ½ tsp black pepper
- 1 clove garlic, minced

Snack: 1 Banana and 1 serving Nut/Seed Butter

- 1 banana
- 1 serving nut/seed butter, approximately 2 tbsp

Fish Taco Salad with Spicy Tomatillo Salsa

- 1 tsp olive oil
- 4 filets of lean white fish, such as cod, tilapia, halibut, mahi mahi etc.
- 1 tsp salt
- ½ tsp pepper
- 1 tsp cumin
- 1 tsp paprika
- 4 cups spinach
- 1 cup cherry tomatoes

For the Spicy Tomatillo Salsa:

- 2 tomatillos
- 2 large tomatoes
- 3 serrano peppers
- 2 limes
- 1 clove garlic
- 1 tsp salt
- ½ tsp black pepper
- 1 bunch cilantro

Jaffa Smoothie

- 1 tbsp chia seeds
- 1 serving chocolate protein powder
- ½ cup oranges, chopped
- 1 cup spinach or kale
- 1 tbsp coconut oil
- 1-2 cups milk of choice, such as almond milk, coconut milk etc. or water
- 1 cup ice

Snack: Apple and Almonds

- ½ medium apple
- 1 serving almond butter

Kale, Cashew & Basil Pesto with Chicken, Zoodles, and Sundried Tomatoes

- 2 tsp olive oil
- Two 8 oz chicken breasts
- **Vegan option:** 1 can chickpeas, drained and rinsed
- 1 tsp salt
- ½ tsp black pepper
- 2 large zucchini
- ½ cup sundried tomatoes, chopped

For the Kale, Cashew & Basil Pesto:

- 2 cups fresh basil leaves
- 2 cups kale, stems removed
- ¼ cup raw cashews
- 1 garlic clove, peeled
- Juice from half of a large lemon
- 1 tsp salt
- ½ tsp black pepper
- ¼ cup extra virgin olive oil

Snack: Celery and Nut/Seed Butter

- 2 tbsp nut/seed butter
- Unlimited celery sticks

Sesame Beef Nourish Bowls

- 1 tsp olive oil
- 1 lb lean ground beef
- A variety of sides such as the following (pick as many as you like):
- 2 cups brown rice
- 2 heads of broccoli, cut into florets
- 4 carrots, sliced
- 1 lb green beans, trimmed and cut into 2" lengths
- 1 can chickpeas, drained and rinsed
- Organic tempeh, cut into 2" cubes
- **Optional toppings:** Sesame seeds, green onions, chopped cashews, spicy chili sauce

For the Sesame Dressing:

- 2 tbsp sesame oil
- ¼ cup reduced sodium soy sauce or coconut aminos
- ¼ cup rice wine vinegar
- ¼ cup olive oil
- 3 tsp garlic powder
- 3 tsp ginger powder
- 1 tbsp stevia, adjust depending on how sweet you like the dressing

Snack: Sugar-Free Coconut Yogurt mixed with Protein Powder

- One 5.3 oz serving of sugar-free coconut yogurt
- ½ serving of great tasting chocolate protein powder
- **Optional toppings:** Berries, coconut flakes, cacao nibs, chopped nuts etc.

Blueberry Pie Smoothie

- 1 tbsp chia seeds
- ¼ cup blueberries, fresh or frozen
- 1 cup greens such as kale or spinach
- 2 cups almond milk
- 1 serving vanilla protein powder
- 1 tsp ground cinnamon + more for sprinkling on top
- 1 tbsp coconut oil
- 1 cup ice

Snack: 2 Mandarins, 1 serving Almonds

- 2 mandarins
- 1 serving of almonds, about ¼ cup

Gado-Gado or Indonesian Steamed Veggie Salad with Peanut Sauce and Chicken

- 1 tsp olive oil
- Two 8 oz chicken breasts, or 8 oz canned chicken
- ½ head green cabbage
- 3 large carrots
- 2 cups green beans
- 1 large sweet potato
- For the Peanut Sauce:
- 1 cup no-sugar peanut butter
- 2 tbsp soy sauce or coconut aminos
- 2 tbsp honey
- 1-2 tbsp spicy chili sauce such as sambal oelek
- ½ lemon, juiced
- 1 garlic clove, minced
- 1 cup water
- **Optional:** 1 cup tofu for the vegan version (V)

Snack: Chocolate Protein Muffins

- 3 very ripe bananas
- 1 tsp baking powder
- ¼ tsp baking soda
- ¼ tsp salt
- ½ cup chocolate protein powder
- 1 tsp vanilla extract
- 2 eggs
- ¼ cup nuts such as pecans, walnuts, etc.
- ¼ cup stevia sweetened chocolate chips, such as Lily's

BBQ Chicken Flatbread

For the Flatbread:

- 1¾ cups of gluten-free flour, such as Bob's Red Mill Gluten Free Flour 1:1 Baking Flour
- 1 tsp baking powder
- 1 tsp salt
- ⅔ cup milk of choice
- ¼ cup olive oil

Toppings:

- 1 cup Marinara sauce, look for a sugar free, preservative free variety
- 1 lb chicken breast, grilled and sliced
- 1 tsp dried oregano
- 1 tsp dried basil
- ½ red onion, finely sliced
- ½ cup sugar free BBQ sauce
- ½ cup cilantro, chopped

Snack: Cookies and Cream Protein Ice Cream

- 1 can full-fat coconut milk
- 1 scoop vanilla flavored protein powder
- 2 tbsp stevia or sweetener or choice
- 1 tsp vanilla extract

For the Cookie Crumbs:

- ¼ cup coconut flour
- 1 scoop chocolate protein powder
- 2 tbsp stevia
- Pinch salt
- 2 tbsp almond butter
- 1 tbsp maple syrup or local honey

Roasted Veggie Souffle

- 1 tbsp olive oil
- 1 small sweet potato, chopped into 1" cubes
- 1 zucchini, chopped into 2" cubes
- 1 large red bell pepper, chopped into 2" cubes
- 1 red onion, sliced
- 1 tsp salt
- ½ tsp black pepper
- 1 tsp garlic powder
- 1 tsp dried oregano
- 1 cup spinach, chopped
- 6 eggs
- ½ cup milk of choice
- 1 tsp salt
- ½ tsp black pepper

Snack: Celery and Nut/Seed Butter

- 2 tbsp nut/seed butter
- Unlimited celery sticks

Shrimp with Avocado, Tomato and Cucumber Salad

- 1 tsp olive oil
- 16 oz shrimp, fresh or frozen
- 1 tsp salt
- ½ tsp pepper
- 4 cups spinach

For the Salad:

- 1 large cucumber
- 1 large tomato
- ½ red onion
- 1 large avocado

For the Dressing:

- ½ lemon, juiced
- ½ cup extra virgin olive oil
- 1 tsp salt
- ½ tsp pepper
- 1 tsp dried oregano

Snack: 1 cup Peaches, 1 serving Almonds

- 1 cup peaches
- 1 serving almonds

Lemon Oregano Chicken with Quinoa

- 4 skinless, boneless chicken breasts
- 1 large lemon
- 1 tbsp olive oil
- 1 tsp salt
- ½ tsp pepper
- 1 tsp dried oregano
- 1 large clove garlic
- 2 cups quinoa
- 4 cups chicken broth + 1 cup chicken broth, divided
- 4 cups spinach
- **Vegan version:** 1 Portobello mushroom cap per person

Snack: Golden Apple Crumble

- 3 apples, cored and diced
- 1 tsp ground turmeric
- 1 + ½ tsp ground cinnamon, divided
- ¼ tsp freshly grated nutmeg
- Pinch of black pepper
- 2 tbsp coconut oil, melted
- 2 tbsp sweetener of choice, like stevia or monkfruit sweetener
- ½ cup gluten free oats

Breakfast

All-the-Greens Smoothie

A green smoothie is the ultimate healthy drink to start the day. We are kicking off Week 3 with this micronutrient-rich green smoothie that will leave you feeling healthy, nourished and energized.

Servings: 1 person

Ingredients:

1 tbsp chia seeds
1 serving vanilla protein powder
½ cup chopped green apple
1 cup spinach or kale
1 stalk celery, chopped
1 cup cucumber, chopped
Juice from half a lemon
1 tbsp coconut oil
1 tsp spirulina, optional
1-2 cups milk of choice, such as almond milk, coconut milk etc. or water
1 cup ice

Instructions:

Put all ingredients into a high-speed blender.

Blend until all ingredients and well combined and there are no chunks.

Pour into a glass and enjoy immediately!

Tip:

Spirulina is blue-green algae that is high in numerous vitamins and minerals. It is often referred to as the most nutrient dense food on the planet. The bright green color of spirulina adds a vibrant hue to the smoothie, as well as B vitamins, copper, iron and phycocyanin, a powerful antioxidant.

Snack

Hummus and Veggies

Servings: 1 person

Make or purchase your favorite hummus and serve with sliced veggies, such as cucumber, celery, carrot sticks, sliced mini bell peppers etc.

See Hummus recipes from Weeks 1 and 2.

Lunch

Asian Slaw with Edamame and Orange

Servings: 4 people

Ingredients:

1 tsp olive oil
2 lbs chicken breast
2 tsp salt
1 tsp black pepper

For the Asian Slaw:

4 cups cabbage, finely sliced
3 carrots, cut into fine matchsticks
½ cup cilantro, chopped
½ cup edamame beans
2 mandarin oranges, segmented
Optional toppings: Sliced almonds, sesame seeds, sliced green onions

For the Asian Slaw Dressing:

1 tbsp sesame oil
1 tsp soy sauce
Juice of 1 lime
½ tsp black pepper
1 clove garlic, minced

Instructions:

Heat a large skillet over a medium heat. Add the olive oil.

Season the chicken breasts with salt and pepper on both sides.

Add the chicken to the hot skillet and allow to cook on one side for about 5 mins, or until the underside is golden brown.

Carefully flip the chicken breasts over and allow to sauté on the second side until golden brown, and the internal temperature is approximately 165° F and completely cooked through.

Meanwhile, add the cabbage, carrots, cilantro and edamame into a large bowl. Toss together to combine thoroughly.

For the dressing, add all the ingredients into a mason jar, tighten the lid onto the jar and then shake to mix completely.

Pour the dressing over the salad and toss altogether.

Scatter the segmented mandarin oranges and any other toppings of choice over the top, such as the sliced almonds, sesame seeds or sliced green onions.

To serve, add a serving of the salad onto a plate with one of the cooked chicken breasts. Enjoy!

Tip:

For the vegan version, omit the chicken and add more edamame to the salad for extra protein and fiber, about ½ cup per person.

1 Banana and 1 serving Nut/Seed Butter

Servings: 1 person

This is a childhood favorite: banana and peanut butter. Of course, depending on what nut or seed butter you use, try to pick something that has no added salt and sugars, since bananas contain natural sugars too.

Ingredients:

1 banana
1 serving nut/seed butter, approximately 2 tbsp

Fish Taco Salad with Spicy Tomatillo Salsa

Servings: 4 people

Ingredients:

1 tsp olive oil
4 filets of lean white fish, such as cod, tilapia, halibut, mahi mahi etc.
1 tsp salt
½ tsp pepper
1 tsp cumin
1 tsp paprika
4 cups spinach
1 cup cherry tomatoes

For the Spicy Tomatillo Salsa:

2 tomatillos
2 large tomatoes
3 serrano peppers
2 limes
1 clove garlic
1 tsp salt
½ tsp black pepper
1 bunch cilantro

Instructions:

For the salsa, put the tomatillos, tomatoes and serrano peppers in a medium saucepan and cover with water. Place a lid on the saucepan and bring to the boil. Reduce heat to a simmer and simmer the veggies until softened.

Drain the water from the saucepan and transfer the veggies to a blender.

Add the garlic clove, salt, pepper and cilantro to the blender.

Blend all the ingredients until desired consistency. I like this salsa quite smooth but with flecks of the cilantro throughout.

Transfer the salsa to a bowl and squeeze in the juice of 1-2 limes, tasting to see if more lime juice or seasoning is needed.

For the fish, add 1 tsp olive oil to a large saucepan and heat on medium high heat on the stove.

While it is heating up, season the fish filets on both sides with salt, pepper, cumin and paprika.

When the pan is hot, carefully place the fish filets into the hot pan and allow to cook for 2-5 minutes, depending on thickness, to develop a golden-brown crust.

Carefully flip the fish over to cook the other side, about 2-5 minutes. Be careful not to overcook the fish.

For tomorrow's meal, take a resealable container and place half of the spinach and cherry tomatoes in it. Top with half of the cooked fish.

For tonight's meal, place the other half of the spinach and cherry tomatoes on a large dinner plate.

Top with the remaining half of the fish and a spoonful or two of the spicy Tomatillo Salsa.

Save the leftovers for tomorrow's dinner!

Tips:

You can choose not to cook all the fish at one time, and simply cook the fish the night you are going to eat it.

Add the Spicy Tomatillo Salsa immediately prior to eating.

To reduce the spice level of the salsa, reduce or remove the serrano peppers from the salsa. You can then chop the serranos and serve as an optional side to the meal.

Breakfast

Jaffa Smoothie

A Jaffa is a candy that I grew up with in New Zealand. They have a fun flavor combo of orange and chocolate that is so delicious! This smoothie is a play on this flavor combo.

Servings: 1 person

Ingredients:

1 tbsp chia seeds
1 serving chocolate protein powder
½ cup oranges, chopped
1 cup spinach or kale
1 tbsp coconut oil
1-2 cups milk of choice, such as almond milk, coconut milk etc. or water
1 cup ice

Instructions:

Put all ingredients into a high-speed blender.

Blend until all ingredients and well combined and there are no chunks.

Pour into a glass and enjoy immediately!

Snack

Apple and Almond Butter

Let the store help you! Easy snack ideas like apple and almond butter, are a great time saver and quick snack when your day is busy, but you still want to fuel your body.

Servings: 1 person

Serving size:

½ medium apple
1 serving almond butter

Lunch

Kale, Cashew & Basil Pesto with Chicken, Zoodles, and Sundried Tomatoes

Servings: 2 people

Instructions:

To make the pesto, add all the ingredients into a food processor. Blend until a thick paste is formed. Taste, and add additional salt and pepper as needed.

To cook chicken, add olive oil to a large saucepan and heat over medium heat on the stove.

Season the chicken breasts with salt and pepper on both sides and add to the hot pan. Cook until the underside is golden brown, about 5 mins.

Carefully flip the chicken, and allow the other side to get golden brown, about 5 mins. Ensure that the chicken breasts are cooked through, or the internal temperature is 165° F.

Meanwhile, use your zoodle machine to make the zucchini into noodles. If you don't have a machine, you can use a vegetable peeler and peel off long thick strands of zucchini.

Place the zoodles in a bowl and add about 1-2 tbsp of pesto. Toss together thoroughly to lightly coat the zoodles.

To serve, add half of the zoodles to a large serving dish. Top with one of the cooked chicken breasts then garnish with ¼ cup of sundried tomatoes to add that pop of color and sweetness. Enjoy!

Grab a resealable container and add the remaining half of the zoodles, the remaining chicken breast and the remaining cherry tomatoes. Close the container and place it in the fridge for tomorrow's dinner.

Ingredients:

2 tsp olive oil
Two 8 oz chicken breasts
Vegan option: 1 can chickpeas, drained and rinsed
1 tsp salt
½ tsp black pepper
2 large zucchini
½ cup sundried tomatoes, chopped

For the Kale Cashew Pesto:

2 cups fresh basil leaves
2 cups kale, stems removed
¼ cup raw cashews
1 garlic clove, peeled
Juice from half of a large lemon
1 tsp salt
½ tsp black pepper
¼ cup extra virgin olive oil

Tip:

For the vegan version use canned chickpeas, instead of chicken, that have been drained and rinsed.

Celery and Nut/Seed Butter

Servings: 1 person

Let the store help you! Easy snack ideas like celery and almond butter, are a great time saver and quick snack when your day is busy, but you still want to fuel your body.

Serving size:

2 tbsp nut/seed butter
Unlimited celery sticks

Sesame Beef Nourish Bowls

Nourish bowls are a great way to incorporate lots of different ingredients into one bowl. I love the idea of having various veggies and proteins prepped then combining them in one bowl with a yummy and healthy sauce.

Servings: 4 people

Ingredients:

1 tsp olive oil
1 lb lean ground beef

A variety of sides such as the following (pick as many as you like):
2 cups brown rice
2 heads of broccoli, cut into florets
4 carrots, sliced
1 lb green beans, trimmed and cut into 2" lengths
1 can chickpeas, drained and rinsed
Organic tempeh, cut into 2" cubes
Optional toppings: Sesame seeds, green onions, chopped cashews, spicy chili sauce

For the Sesame Dressing:

2 tbsp sesame oil
¼ cup reduced sodium soy sauce or coconut aminos
¼ cup rice wine vinegar
¼ cup olive oil
3 tsp garlic powder
3 tsp ginger powder
1 tbsp stevia, adjust depending on how sweet you like the dressing

Instructions:

For the beef: Heat 1 tsp olive oil in a large sauté pan over medium heat.

One the pan is hot, add the ground beef and cook until completely cooked through.

For the sides:

Brown rice: Rinse the rice in a colander to remove extra starch. Watch for and remove any foreign objects like little stones.

Take a large pot and add the brown rice. Pour in 6 cups of water.

Bring to the boil over high heat, then reduce heat to low and simmer until completely cooked, approximately 30-45 mins.

Broccoli: Cut the florets off of the broccoli and steam in the microwave for approximately 3-4 mins.

Carrots: Cut the carrots into slices and steam in the microwave for approximately 3-4 mins.

Green beans: Trim the ends off the green beans, cut into 2" sections and steam in the microwave for approximately 3-4 mins.

Chickpeas: Drain and rinse chickpeas.

Tempeh: Cut tempeh into 2" cubes.

Heat a medium saucepan over medium high heat, add 1 tsp olive oil and the tempeh. Cook until tempeh is golden brown all over.

For the dressing: add all the ingredients into a mason jar and screw the lid on tightly. Vigorously shake the jar to combine all the ingredients thoroughly.

To make the Sesame Beef Nourish Bowls, add your choice of sides to a bowl, such as 1 serving each of brown rice, broccoli, carrots, green beans, chickpeas and tempeh.

Drizzle over 1-2 tbsp of the dressing and top with your favorite toppings like sesame seeds, chopped green onions and/or cashews.

Cool the remaining ingredients then store in the fridge for another meal. Alternatively, you can opt to make some more nourish bowls in resealable containers (using the previous two steps as a guide) and keep them in the fridge for future meals.

Tip:

For the vegan version, omit the beef and focus on having the tempeh and chickpeas as your protein source.

Wednesday/Thursday

Snack

Sugar-Free Coconut Yogurt mixed with Protein Powder

As an extra protein-rich snack, try this vegan coconut yogurt mixed with chocolate protein powder. The protein powder will not only fill up your belly, but it will also add that delicious flavor of chocolate to guilt-free dessert.

Serving size: 1 person

Ingredients:

One 5.3 oz serving of sugar-free coconut yogurt
½ serving of great tasting chocolate protein powder
Optional toppings: Berries, coconut flakes, cacao nibs, chopped nuts etc.

Instructions:

In a medium sized bowl, add the yogurt and protein powder. Mix very well until fully combined.

Transfer to your serving bowl, and top with your fave toppings such as berries, coconut flakes, nuts etc.

Friday/Saturday

Breakfast

Blueberry Pie Smoothie

Servings: 1 person

Ingredients:

1 tbsp chia seeds
¼ cup blueberries, fresh or frozen
1 cup greens such as kale or spinach
2 cups almond milk
1 serving vanilla protein powder
1 tsp ground cinnamon + more for sprinkling on top
1 tbsp coconut oil
1 cup ice

Instructions:

Place all ingredients into a high-speed blender.

Blend until completely smooth.

Pour into your serving glass and sprinkle on a bit more cinnamon.

Enjoy immediately!

Snack

2 Mandarins, 1 serving Almonds

I always seem to have mandarins in the house because of the kids. I love to pair them with a healthy protein and fat source like nuts to help keep me satiated.

Servings: 1 person

Ingredients:

2 mandarins
1 serving of almonds, about ¼ cup

Lunch

Gado-Gado or Indonesian Steamed Veggie Salad with Peanut Sauce and Chicken

This is one of my favorite Indonesian dishes. Gado-gado means "mixture" and refers to the mixture of steamed vegetables used in the dish. The Peanut Sauce used to dress the steamed vegetables can also be used with spring rolls, summer rolls and almost any kind of protein.

Servings: 2 people

Ingredients:

1 tsp olive oil
Two 8 oz chicken breasts, or 8 oz canned chicken
½ head green cabbage
3 large carrots
2 cups green beans
1 large sweet potato

For the Peanut Sauce:

1 cup no-sugar peanut butter
2 tbsp soy sauce or coconut aminos
2 tbsp honey
1-2 tbsp spicy chili sauce such as sambal oelek
½ lemon, juiced
1 garlic clove, minced
1 cup water
Optional: 1 cup tofu for the vegan version (V)

Instructions:

Heat a large non-stick pan on a medium heat with 1 tsp olive oil.

Season the chicken breasts with salt and pepper on both sides and add to the hot pan. Cook until the underside is golden brown, about 5 mins.

Carefully flip the chicken, and allow the other side to get golden brown, about 5 mins. Ensure that the chicken breasts are cooked through, or the internal temperature is 165° F.

While the chicken is cooking, cut the sweet potato into 1" cubes and steam in the microwave until tender.

Finely slice the cabbage and steam in the microwave until tender.

Cut the carrots into matchsticks and steam in the microwave until tender.

Trim the stalk ends from the green beans and steam in the microwave until tender.

Grab a resealable container and place half of the veggies in the container. This will be for tomorrow's lunch.

For the peanut sauce, combine all the ingredients in a small pot and heat over a medium low heat on the stove. Stir to combine thoroughly. Taste and adjust the seasoning as desired.

Once the chicken breasts are cooked through, place one chicken breast on the serving plate with the other half of your steamed veggies.

Drizzle over 1-2 tbsp of the peanut sauce and enjoy!

Allow the second chicken breast to cool before placing in the resealable container. Then close the container and place in the fridge for tomorrow's lunch.

Tip:

For the vegan version, grill or sauté approximately 8 oz firm tofu in a saucepan with about 1 tsp olive oil, until it is golden brown. Turn over and cook until golden-brown.

Snack

Chocolate Protein Muffins

These muffins are made with no refined flour. Be sure to use a protein powder that you enjoy the flavor of, as this will help ensure your muffins are absolutely delicious!

Servings: 8-10 muffins depending on size

Ingredients:

3 very ripe bananas
1 tsp baking powder
¼ tsp baking soda
¼ tsp salt
½ cup chocolate protein powder
1 tsp vanilla extract
2 eggs
¼ cup nuts such as pecans, walnuts, etc.
¼ cup stevia sweetened chocolate chips, such as Lily's

Instructions:

Preheat the oven to 350° F.

Line a muffin pan with liner cups or grease with a non-stick spray.

In a large bowl, add the bananas and mash with a fork until totally smooth.

Add in the eggs and vanilla extract. Mix together thoroughly.

Add in the baking powder, baking soda, salt, and protein powder. Combine well.

Fold in the nuts and chocolate chips.

Scoop the batter into the muffin cups. Try to fill each muffin cup to about two-thirds full.

Bake in a preheated oven for approximately 15-20 mins, or until a toothpick inserted in the center comes out with a couple of moist crumbs attached.

Tip:

Cool then store in an airtight container in the fridge for up to a week.

Dinner

BBQ Chicken Flatbread

Servings: 4 people

Ingredients:

For the Flatbread:

1¾ cups of gluten-free flour, such as Bob's Red Mill Gluten Free Flour 1:1 Baking Flour
1 tsp baking powder
1 tsp salt
⅔ cup milk of choice
¼ cup olive oil

Toppings:

1 cup Marinara sauce, look for a sugar free, preservative free variety
1 lb chicken breast, grilled and sliced
1 tsp dried oregano
1 tsp dried basil
½ red onion, finely sliced
½ cup sugar-free BBQ sauce
½ cup cilantro, chopped

Instructions:

Preheat the oven to 425° F.

Grease a cookie sheet with a little olive oil.

In a large bowl, combine the flour, baking powder and salt, and mix thoroughly.

Add in the milk and olive oil, and stir until a soft ball of dough forms. You may need to use your hands to press the ball together.

Place the dough onto a greased cookie sheet and use your fingers to press it out to a round shape. Alternatively, flour your working space and roll the dough out using a rolling pin until it is the desired size. Transfer to a greased cookie sheet.

Top the flatbread with the marinara sauce, chicken, red onion, dried oregano and basil.

Place in a preheated 425° F oven on the middle rack for approximately 20 mins until the edges are golden and the bottom of the flatbread is cooked through.

Remove the flatbread from the oven. Drizzle over the BBQ sauce and scatter over the chopped cilantro.

Slice and serve immediately, alongside your favorite salad or veggies of choice.

W ho doesn't love some ice cream? This take on Cookies and Cream includes faux cookie crumbles, which are super easy to make and taste delicious.

Snack

Cookies and Cream Protein Ice Cream

Servings: 4 people

Ingredients:

1 can full-fat coconut milk
1 scoop vanilla flavored protein powder
2 tbsp stevia or sweetener or choice
1 tsp vanilla extract

For the Cookie Crumbs:

¼ cup coconut flour
1 scoop chocolate protein powder
2 tbsp stevia
Pinch salt
2 tbsp almond butter
1 tbsp maple syrup or local honey

Instructions:

For the cookie crumbs, mix all the dry ingredients together thoroughly. Then add the wet ingredients (almond butter and maple syrup or honey) to create cookie crumbs as big or as little as you like.

In a blender, add all the other ingredients and blend until thoroughly combined.

Pour into an ice cream maker and allow to churn per the manufacturer instructions.

After churning the ice cream in the ice cream maker, add in ¾ of the cookie crumbs and fold into the ice cream. Sprinkle over the remaining cookie crumbs.

If a firmer consistency of ice cream is desired, transfer the ice cream to a freezer-safe container and place in the freezer for 1-2 hours.

Tip:

This ice cream is best served soon after making it. If you have set the ice cream in the freezer for too long, allow to thaw slightly at room temperature until at the desired softness.

Breakfast

Roasted Veggie Souffle

Servings: 6 people

Sometimes a warm and comforting eggy breakfast is exactly what the doctor ordered! This baked egg souffle is filled with lots of yummy roasted veg, to give you delicious micronutrients and fiber to keep you feeling fuller for longer.

Ingredients:

1 tbsp olive oil
1 small sweet potato, chopped into 1" cubes
1 zucchini, chopped into 2" cubes
1 large red bell pepper, chopped into 2" cubes
1 red onion, sliced
1 tsp salt
½ tsp black pepper
1 tsp garlic powder
1 tsp dried oregano

1 cup spinach, chopped
6 eggs
½ cup milk of choice
1 tsp salt
½ tsp black pepper

Instructions:

Preheat the oven to 420° F.

To a large baking tray, add the chopped veggies, olive oil, salt, pepper, garlic powder and dried oregano.

Toss to combine.

Roast the veggies in a preheated oven for approximately 20 mins or until cooked through and caramelized on the edges.

Remove from the oven and allow to cool slightly.

Meanwhile, in a large bowl, crack the eggs, and add the milk, salt and pepper.

Whisk together until completely combined.

Add in the chopped spinach and mix again.

Take 6 ramekins and lightly grease with olive oil or a non-stick spray.

Carefully transfer the roasted veggies into the ramekins. Try to make sure each ramekin has some of each veggie and the veggies are divided evenly between all the ramekins.

Pour the egg mixture over the top of the veggies in each ramekin. Fill to approximately ¾ full.

Bake the egg souffles in the 420° F preheated oven for approximately 20 mins, until the egg is puffy and cooked through.

Remove from the oven and allow to cool slightly before serving with a fresh green salad.

Sunday

Snack

Celery and Nut/Seed Butter

Servings: 1

2 tbsp nut/seed butter
Unlimited celery sticks

Tip: Sunday Selfcare

Spend a little time each week on you! Self care is a wonderful way to refill your proverbial cup. You can decompress from the week, unwind in a bubble bath, go for a walk in nature, read your favorite book or anything else you feel like doing. The key is to listen to your body, mind and spirit, and to do what you need to feel fulfilled.

Selfcare helps you to relieve any stress you may be experiencing which also has a huge impact on your gut, emotional and mental health.

There are so many benefits to selfcare so be sure to schedule time into your week for some you-time!

Sunday

Dinner

Shrimp with Avocado, Tomato and Cucumber Salad

Servings: 2 people

Ingredients:

1 tsp olive oil
16 oz shrimp, fresh or frozen
1 tsp salt
½ tsp pepper
4 cups spinach

For the Salad:

1 large cucumber
1 large tomato
½ red onion
1 large avocado

For the Dressing:

½ lemon, juiced
½ cup extra virgin olive oil
1 tsp salt
½ tsp pepper
1 tsp dried oregano

Instructions:

Heat 1 tsp olive oil in a large sauté pan over medium heat.

Once the pan is hot, add the shrimp and quickly season with salt and pepper.

Stir until cooked through and remove from the heat.

For the salad: chop the cucumber, tomatoes and avocado into bite sized pieces. Add to a large bowl.

Finely slice the red onion and add to the bowl as well.

For the dressing: add all ingredients into a mason jar. Tightly screw on the lid and shake vigorously to thoroughly combine the ingredients.

Drizzle the dressing over the salad and gently toss to combine.

To serve, add 2 cups of spinach onto a large plate, top with half of the Avocado, Tomato and Cucumber salad. Place half of the shrimp on the plate and enjoy!

Cool the remaining shrimp, then in a resealable container, add the spinach, the remaining salad and shrimp. Close the lid tightly, then keep in the fridge for dinner tomorrow.

1 cup Peaches, 1 serving Almonds

Fresh seasonal fruit is a great way to curb that sweet tooth. Look for seasonal fruit depending on where you are in the world and what time of year it is.

Servings: 1 person

1 cup peaches
1 serving almonds

Lemon Oregano Chicken with Quinoa

This is one of my fave sheet pan dinners and one that my clients love! So great for the whole family and so easy to make and clean up. What could be better than that?

Servings: 4 people

Ingredients:

4 skinless, boneless chicken breasts
1 large lemon
1 tbsp olive oil
1 tsp salt
½ tsp pepper
1 tsp dried oregano
1 large clove garlic
2 cups quinoa
4 cups chicken broth + 1 cup chicken broth, divided
4 cups spinach
Vegan version: 1 Portobello mushroom cap per person

Instructions:

Add the quinoa and 4 cups chicken broth to a medium saucepan and cover with a lid.

Bring the quinoa to a boil, then reduce to a simmer, until the quinoa has absorbed all the liquid. Heat 1 tbsp olive oil in a large nonstick pan on medium high heat.

Season the chicken breasts with salt and pepper on both sides.

When the pan is hot, add the chicken breasts and sauté until golden brown on one side, about 3-5 mins until golden brown. Turn the chicken breasts over, then cook on the other side for another 3-5 mins.

Once the chicken is cooked, remove it from the pan and reduce the heat to medium. Add the garlic. Sauté, stirring frequently, until aromatic, about 1 minute.

Squeeze in the juice of 1 lemon, the dried oregano and 1 cup chicken broth. Stir together until bubbling. Add the chicken breast back into the sauce and simmer until fully cooked, or until the internal temperature is 165° F.

To serve, place 1 cup of spinach onto a plate. Add 1 serving of quinoa, then top with 1 chicken breast and some of the sauce.

Tip:

For the vegan version, use large Portobello mushrooms, in place of the chicken and vegetable stock in place of the chicken stock. Portobello mushrooms are very hearty and have almost a meaty texture.

Sunday

Snack

Golden Apple Crumble

Servings: 4 people

Ingredients:

3 apples, cored and diced
1 tsp ground turmeric
1 + ½ tsp ground cinnamon, divided
¼ tsp freshly grated nutmeg
Pinch of black pepper
2 tbsp coconut oil, melted
2 tbsp sweetener of choice, like stevia or
   monkfruit sweetener
½ cup gluten free oats

Instructions:

Preheat oven to 400° F.

In a pie dish, add the diced apples and sprinkle with turmeric, ½ tsp ground cinnamon, nutmeg and a pinch of black pepper.

In a small bowl, mix together the oats, coconut oil, 1 tsp ground cinnamon, and sweetener of choice.

Sprinkle the oat mixture on top of the apples in the pie dish.

Bake for approximately 30 mins until apples are softened and oats are golden-brown.

Serve with protein ice cream and an extra dash of cinnamon.

Sometimes we just need a simple baked treat to help us feel comforted and cozy. This Golden Apple Crumble is just that! The apples are infused with the same aromatic spices you would see in golden milk. These spices also give the apples a beautiful golden color, as well as anti-inflammatory and antioxidant properties. It's the perfect healthy dessert way to end your third week of meal plans!

Week 4

Woohoo! You've made it to Week 4! You have done an incredible job during the last 3 weeks and this week will be the icing on the cake! Keep up the great work! Keep eating the foods that fuel you, keep prepping your food and keep building these healthy sustainable habits!

Week 4 Meal Plan
At A Glance

	Monday/ Tuesday	Wednesday/ Thursday	Friday/ Saturday	Sunday
Breakfast	Peach Ginger Smoothie (V)	Cherry Pie Smoothie (V)	Cookies and Cream Smoothie (V)	Everything Bagel Poached Egg Stacks (V: Roasted Tomatoes)
Snack	Hummus and Veggies (V)	½ cup Strawberries, 1 serving Almonds	Celery and Nut/Seed Butter (V)	Oatmeal Raisin Protein Bars (V)
Lunch	Superfood Falafels (V)	Chicken, Apple, Kale and Portobello Mushroom Salad	Broccoli and Asparagus Soup with Roasted Chickpeas (V)	Sheet Pan Chicken Shwarmas
Snack	1 Green Apple and Nut/Seed Butter (V)	Hummus and Veggies (V)	1 Green Apple and Nut/Seed Butter (V)	½ cup Cherries, 1 serving almonds
Dinner	Egg Roll in a Bowl (V: Tempeh)	Paleo Pad Thai with Chicken (V: Tofu)	Crockpot Mongolian Beef with Brown Rice (V: Tofu)	Hawaiian Chicken Skewers with Quinoa (V: Chickpeas)
Snack	1 serving Almonds	1 cup Berries (V)	Chocolate Coconut Chia Seed Pudding (V)	Molten Chocolate Mug Cake (V: Chia Seed Egg)

(V) indicates a Vegan recipe or option for the meal.

Week 4 Grocery List

Peach Ginger Smoothie

- 1 tbsp chia seeds
- ¼ cup peaches, fresh or frozen
- 1 serving vanilla protein powder
- 1 cup greens such as kale, spinach etc.
- 1 tbsp healthy fats such as nut butter, avocado etc.
- ½ tsp ground ginger
- 2 cups water
- 1 cup ice

Snack: Hummus and Veggies

- 2 tbsp hummus
- Unlimited veggies for dipping!

Superfood Falafels

- One 15-oz can chickpeas, drained and rinsed
- 1 cup fresh kale, lightly packed
- 1 cup fresh cilantro, lightly packed
- 1 tsp salt
- ½ tsp ground black pepper
- 1 garlic clove, peeled
- 1 tsp ground coriander
- 2 tsp cumin
- 2 tbsp hemp hearts
- 2 tbsp chia seeds
- 1 tbsp olive oil

Snack: Apple and Nut/Seed Butter

- 1 medium green apple
- 2 tbsp nut/seed butter

Egg Roll in a Bowl

- 1 tsp olive oil
- 2 cloves garlic, minced
- 1½ tbsp fresh ginger, minced; or use ½ tsp ground ginger
- ½ lb ground beef or turkey
- 2 cups green cabbage, sliced finely
- 1 cup spinach
- 1 cup carrots, finely sliced
- ⅛ cup coconut aminos or soy sauce
- 1 tsp sesame oil
- 2 green onions, chopped
- 2 tbsp chopped peanuts
- **Vegan option:** 16 oz organic tofu

Snack: 1 serving Almonds

- 1 serving almonds

Cherry Pie Smoothie

- 1 tbsp chia seeds
- ¼ cup cherries, fresh or frozen
- 1 cup greens such as kale or spinach
- 2 cups water
- 1 serving vanilla protein powder
- 1 tbsp coconut oil
- 1 cup ice

Snack: ½ cup Strawberries, 1 serving Almonds

- ½ cup strawberries
- 1 serving raw almonds, approx. ¼ cup

Chicken, Apple, Kale and Portobello Mushroom Salad

- 1 tsp olive oil
- 16 oz chicken breast, or canned and drained chicken
- 8 cups baby kale
- 1 green apple, chopped into bite sized pieces.
- 2 Portobello mushrooms, sliced
- **Vegan option:** 2 cups chickpeas

For the Dressing:

- ½ lemon, juiced
- ½ cup extra virgin olive oil
- 1 tsp salt
- ½ tsp pepper
- 1 tsp dried rosemary, crushed between your fingers

Snack: Hummus and Veggies

- 2 tbsp hummus
- Unlimited veggies for dipping

Paleo Pad Thai

- 2-3 medium zucchini made into noodles i.e. zoodles
- 4 tablespoons raw agave or honey
- 4 tablespoons soy sauce or coconut aminos
- 4 tablespoons distilled white vinegar or rice wine vinegar
- 2-4 tsp sesame oil, to taste
- 3 tablespoons vegetable oil
- 16 oz sliced chicken breast
- 2 eggs
- 2 cups spinach or kale
- 2 tablespoons crushed roasted peanuts
- 1 teaspoon dried Thai birds eye chili or chili flakes or sriracha
- Cilantro, roughly chopped
- Lime wedges
- **Vegan option:** Organic tempeh

Snack: 1 cup Berries

- 1 cup berries of choice

Cookies and Cream Smoothie

For the Smoothie:

- 1 tbsp chia seeds
- 1 cup greens, like spinach or kale
- 1 tbsp healthy fats e.g. nut/seed butter, avocado
- 1 serving vanilla protein powder
- 1-2 cups milk of choice, e.g. almond milk, coconut milk etc.
- 1 cup ice

For the Cookie Crumbs:

- ¼ cup coconut flour
- ½ scoop chocolate protein powder
- 1 tbsp stevia
- Pinch salt
- ½ tbsp maple syrup, or other liquid sweetener
- 1 tbsp nut/seed butter

Snack: Celery and Nut/Seed Butter

- 2 tbsp nut/seed butter
- Unlimited celery sticks

Broccoli and Asparagus Soup

- 1 tbsp olive oil
- 1 onion, chopped
- 2 cloves of garlic, minced
- 4 cups broccoli stalks, roughly chopped
- 2 cups asparagus stalks
- 6 cups chicken bone broth
- 1 tsp salt
- ½ tsp black pepper
- 1 tbsp dried rosemary
- 1 tsp dried thyme leaves

Snack: Apple and Almond Butter

- 1 medium apple
- 2 tbsp almond butter

Crockpot Mongolian Beef with Brown Rice

- 2 cups brown rice
- 5 cups water
- 2 lbs flank steak, sliced into thin strips
- ¾ cup reduced sodium soy sauce or coconut aminos
- ¾ cup water
- ½ cup stevia or monkfruit sweetener
- 1 cup carrots, cut into matchsticks
- 3 green onions, chopped
- **Vegan option:** Organic firm tofu

Chocolate Coconut Chia Seed Pudding

- ⅓ cup chia seeds
- ¼ cup hemp hearts
- 1 scoop Chocolate Protein Powder
- One 13 oz can coconut milk
- ½ cup milk of choice, such as almond milk or coconut milk
- ¼ cup unsweetened desiccated coconut
- **Toppings:** Chopped pistachios, chopped dried apricots, unsweetened dessicated coconut, cacao nibs

Everything Bagel Poached Egg Stacks and Avocado Mash

For the Sweet Potato Toasts:

- 1 large sweet potato, washed and cut into 1" thick rounds
- ½ tbsp olive oil
- ½ tsp Everything Bagel seasoning

For the Kale Salad:

- 4 cups of kale, washed and finely sliced
- 1 tbsp fresh lemon juice
- 1 tsp olive oil
- Pinch of salt and pepper

For the Avocado Mash:

- 1 large avocado
- ½ tbsp lemon juice
- 1 tbsp nutritional yeast
- ½ tsp kosher or smoked salt

For the Poached Eggs:

- 4 eggs
- 1 tsp white vinegar

For the Vegan Option:

- 2 large beefsteak tomatoes
- 1 tbsp olive oil
- ½ tsp salt
- ¼ tsp black pepper

Oatmeal Raisin Protein Bars

- ⅔ cup oats
- ½ cup nut/seed butter e.g. almond butter, peanut butter or tahini
- 2 tbsp honey, or liquid sweetener of choice
- ¼ cup vanilla protein powder of choice
- 1 tsp vanilla extract
- 2 tbsp raisins

Sheet Pan Chicken Shwarmas

- 3 lbs chicken breast, sliced into ½" thick slices
- 1 large red onion, sliced thickly
- 2 large bell peppers, any color, sliced thickly
- 2 large zucchini, chopped into 2" cubes
- 1 large sweet potato, chopped into 2" cubes
- 1 tbsp olive oil
- 1 tsp paprika
- 1 tsp turmeric
- 1 tsp ground cumin
- ¼ tsp ground cinnamon
- 1 tsp dried oregano
- 1 tsp salt
- ½ tsp black pepper
- To serve, your choice of hummus, green salad, quinoa/rice etc.

Snack: ½ cup Cherries, 1 serving Almonds

- ½ cup fresh cherries
- 1 serving almonds

Hawaiian Chicken Skewers with Quinoa

For the Marinade:

- 1 cup sugar-free BBQ sauce
- ¼ cup pineapple juice
- 1 tbsp soy sauce alternative
- 2 cloves garlic, minced
- ¼ cup cilantro, roughly chopped
- 1" piece of fresh ginger, grated
- ¼ tsp black pepper
- 2 lbs chicken breast, cut into 1" cubes
- 2 bell peppers, any color, cut into 1" pieces
- 1 pineapple, cut into 1" pieces

For the Quinoa Salad:

- 1 cup quinoa
- 2 cups chicken stock
- ¼ cup fresh cilantro, roughly chopped
- 2 green onions, greens finely chopped
- 1 tbsp sesame seeds

Molten Chocolate Mug Cake

- 1 scoop or ¼ cup chocolate protein powder
- 1 tbsp almond flour
- ½ tsp baking powder
- ½ tsp vanilla extract
- 1 egg
- 1 tbsp milk, you may need to add more milk depending on absorbency of your protein powder
- 1 tbsp monkfruit sweetener
- **Optional topping:** eg 1 tbsp nut butter, or jam

Breakfast

Peach Ginger Smoothie

Servings: 1 person

Ingredients:

1 tbsp chia seeds
¼ cup peaches, fresh or frozen
1 serving vanilla protein powder
1 cup greens such as kale, spinach etc.
1 tbsp healthy fats such as nut butter, avocado etc.
½ tsp ground ginger
2 cups water
1 cup ice

Instructions:

Put all ingredients into a high-speed blender.

Blend until all ingredients are well combined and there are no chunks.

Enjoy immediately!

Tips:

To meal prep a smoothie, place the ingredients for the smoothie (except the liquid and ice) into a small ziploc bag and place in the fridge or freezer.

Use greens powder and/or fiber powder in the smoothie for added nutritional benefits.

Snack

Hummus and Veggies

If you don't feel like making your own hummus, purchase hummus from the grocery store and even some pre-washed and chopped veggies for dipping. The store is your best resource for helping to make your healthy eating choices even easier.

Servings: 1 person

Serving Size:

2 tbsp hummus
Unlimited veggies for dipping!

Lunch

Superfood Falafels

Servings: 2 people

Ingredients:

One 15 oz can chickpeas, drained and
    rinsed
1 cup fresh kale, lightly packed
1 cup fresh cilantro, lightly packed
1 tsp salt
½ tsp ground black pepper

1 garlic clove, peeled
1 tsp ground coriander
2 tsp cumin
2 tbsp hemp hearts
2 tbsp chia seeds
1 tbsp olive oil

Instructions:

Add the chickpeas, kale, cilantro, salt, pepper, garlic, coriander, cumin, hemp hearts and chia seeds to a high-speed blender or food processor.

Blend until all the ingredients are combined but still with a slightly chunky texture. You may need to scrape down the insides of the blender/food processor several times to combine the mixture.

Preheat the oven to 400° F.

Grease an oven tray with olive oil.

Take 2 tbsp of the falafel mixture and roll it into a ball. Place the ball onto the prepared tray and gently press down with your fingers, to flatten into a disc. Repeat with remaining falafel mixture.

If the mixture is too dry to hold together, add water about 1 tbsp at a time, and mix well. See if the mixture will hold together. If not, continue adding water 1 tbsp at a time then mix together again.

If the mixture is too wet, you can add flour, 1 tbsp at a time, to help to absorb some of the moisture.

Bake the falafels in a preheated oven for approximately 20 mins, or until crispy and golden brown. Flip over, then bake for another 10-15 mins until the other side is golden brown too.

Serve falafels warm with hummus or tzatziki, and a nice fresh green salad!

Snack

Apple and Nut/Seed Butter

Servings: 1 person

Serving size:

1 medium green apple
2 tbsp nut/seed butter

Dinner

Egg Roll in a Bowl

This is one of the easiest dinner recipes and a favorite amongst my clients. It's all you love about an egg roll, but without that pesky dough to roll and deep fry.

Tip:

Add the sesame oil, green onions and chopped peanuts right before serving. For the vegan option, feel free to replace the meat with organic tofu cut into 1" cubes.

Servings: 2

Ingredients:

1 tsp olive oil
2 cloves garlic, minced
1½ tbsp fresh ginger, minced; or use ½ tsp ground ginger
½ lb ground beef or turkey
2 cups green cabbage, sliced finely
1 cup spinach

1 cup carrots, finely sliced
⅛ cup coconut aminos or soy sauce
1 tsp sesame oil
2 green onions, chopped
2 tbsp chopped peanuts
Vegan option: 16 oz organic tofu

Instructions:

Add 1 tsp olive oil to a large saucepan and heat on medium high heat on the stove.

Add the ground beef or turkey and sauté until cooked through. Add the garlic and ginger, and stir until fragrant, about 1 minute. Add in the cabbage, carrots, spinach and coconut aminos/soy sauce. Stir until cabbage is tender, about 5-10 mins.

Divide the recipe in half. Transfer one serving to an airtight container to be cooled and kept in the fridge until tomorrow's dinner.

Transfer the remaining half of the recipe to a serving bowl. Garnish with ½ tsp sesame oil, green onions and chopped peanuts. Enjoy immediately!

Snack

1 serving Almonds

Servings: 1 person

1 serving almonds

Breakfast

Cherry Pie Smoothie

Servings: 1 person

Ingredients:

1 tbsp chia seeds
¼ cup cherries, fresh or frozen
1 cup greens such as kale or spinach
2 cups water

1 serving vanilla protein powder
1 tbsp coconut oil
1 cup ice

Instructions:

Place all ingredients into a high-speed blender. Blend until completely smooth.

Pour into your serving glass. Enjoy immediately!

Snack

½ cup Strawberries, 1 serving Almonds

This snack is an awesome way to curb that sweet tooth while also getting some healthy fats and protein too.

Servings: 1 person

Ingredients:

½ cup strawberries
1 serving raw almonds, approx. ¼ cup

Lunch

Chicken, Apple, Kale and Portobello Mushroom Salad

Servings: 2 people

Instructions:

Add olive oil to a large saucepan and heat over medium heat on the stove.

Season the chicken breasts with salt and pepper on both sides and add to the hot pan. Cook until the underside is golden brown, about 5 mins.

Carefully flip the chicken, and allow the other side to get golden brown, about 5 mins. Ensure that the chicken breasts are cooked through, or the internal temperature is 165° F.

Remove the chicken from the pan and add in the sliced portobello mushrooms. Sauté until softened, about 5 mins.

For the dressing, add all ingredients into a small jar. Put the lid on the jar and shake vigorously to combine.

For the salad, add 4 cups of baby kale onto a large serving plate. Add the remaining greens in a resealable container for tomorrow's lunch. Top the greens with half of the chopped apple, sautéed mushrooms and chicken. Do the same for the greens in the resealable container.

Drizzle the dressing over the salad on the serving plate and enjoy! Close the resealable container and place in the fridge for tomorrow's lunch.

Ingredients:

1 tsp olive oil
16 oz chicken breast, or canned and drained chicken
8 cups baby kale
1 green apple, chopped into bite sized pieces.
2 portobello mushrooms, sliced
Vegan option: 2 cups chickpeas

For the Dressing:

½ lemon, juiced
½ cup extra virgin olive oil
1 tsp salt
½ tsp pepper
1 tsp dried rosemary, crushed between your fingers

Tips:

For the vegan option, simply leave out the chicken.

Snack

Hummus and Veggies

Serving size: 1 person

2 tbsp hummus
Unlimited veggies for dipping

Dinner

Paleo Pad Thai

Ingredients:

2-3 medium zucchini made into noodles i.e. zoodles
4 tablespoons raw agave or honey
4 tablespoons soy sauce or coconut aminos
4 tablespoons distilled white vinegar or rice wine vinegar
2-4 tsp sesame oil, to taste
3 tablespoons vegetable oil
16 oz sliced chicken breast
2 eggs
2 cups spinach or kale
2 tablespoons crushed roasted peanuts
1 teaspoon dried Thai birds eye chili or chili flakes or sriracha
Cilantro, roughly chopped
lime wedges
Vegan option: Organic tempeh

Servings: 4 people

Instructions:

In a small bowl, stir together the agave, soy sauce, sesame oil and vinegar to make a sauce.

Heat a wok or large saucepan over high heat until it is super hot, then swirl in the oil. Once the oil is hot, add the chicken and stir-fry until golden, about 5 minutes. You may need to do this in batches.

Add the zoodles and the sauce, then continue to stir-fry, constantly stirring, until the noodles absorb the sauce, about another minute.

Push the noodle mixture to one side of the pan and leave them there, making an empty space in the center of the wok/saucepan. Crack the eggs into the empty space and let it cook without stirring until the edges start to set, 15 to 20 seconds. Use a spatula to break up and roughly scramble the eggs, then toss it back in with the noodles while the egg is still soft.

Once the eggs look mostly cooked, remove the pan from the heat and throw in the spinach or kale, tossing thoroughly to combine. Transfer to a plate and garnish with the peanuts, chilies, cilantro, and lime wedges.

Tip:

For the vegan option, use organic tempeh in place of the chicken. Cook in the same manner as the chicken to get the tempeh golden brown. You can also omit the eggs.

Snack

1 cup Berries

Servings: 1 person

1 cup berries of choice

Breakfast

Cookies and Cream Smoothie

Servings: 1 person

Ingredients:

For the Smoothie:

1 tbsp chia seeds
1 cup greens, like spinach or kale
1 tbsp healthy fats e.g. nut/seed butter, avocado
1 serving vanilla protein powder
1-2 cups milk of choice, e.g. almond milk, coconut milk etc.
1 cup ice

For the Cookie Crumbs:

¼ cup coconut flour
½ scoop chocolate protein powder
1 tbsp stevia
Pinch salt
½ tbsp maple syrup, or other liquid sweetener
1 tbsp nut/seed butter

Instructions:

Place all of the smoothie ingredients into a high-speed blender.

Blend until completely smooth.

To make the cookie crumbs, mix all the dry ingredients together. Add the wet ingredients into the mixture and create cookie crumbs by mixing the wet ingredients into the dry ingredients. The cookie crumbs can be as big or as little as you like.

Pour the smoothie into a glass and sprinkle over some cookie crumbs. You can even mix some cookie crumbs into the smoothie too. Enjoy immediately!

Snack

Celery and Nut/Seed Butter

Servings: 1 person

2 tbsp nut/seed butter
Unlimited celery sticks

Lunch

Broccoli and Asparagus Soup

This is a fantastic way to use up broccoli stalks and asparagus stalks. These stalks are often tougher, so people generally throw them away. But softening them in some bone broth and then puréeing them makes a thick and creamy soup. Now you just have to decide what you're going to dip into the soup!

Servings: 4 people

Ingredients:

1 tbsp olive oil
1 onion, chopped
2 cloves of garlic, minced
4 cups broccoli stalks, roughly chopped
2 cups asparagus stalks
6 cups chicken bone broth
1 tsp salt
½ tsp black pepper
1 tbsp dried rosemary
1 tsp dried thyme leaves

Instructions:

Place a large pot with a lid, over a medium heat. Add olive oil.

Once the pot and olive oil are warm, add the onions, and sauté until softened, about 5 mins.

Add the minced garlic, and sauté for approximately 1 minute or until fragrant.

Add the broccoli stalks, asparagus stalks and chicken bone broth. Stir gently together to incorporate.

Increase the heat to medium high and bring the soup to a boil. Reduce to a simmer and cover the pot with the lid. Simmer until the vegetables are tender, about 15-20 mins.

Using an immersion blender, or a high-speed blender, purée the soup until creamy. You may have to do this in batches if using a high-speed blender. See Tips when blending hot liquids.

Return the soup to the pot, if using a blender, taste and season with additional salt and pepper if desired.

Serve warm.

Tips:

Be extra careful when blending hot liquids. Here are a few things to remember:

Only fill the blender half full with the hot or warm liquid. When we blend hot liquids, it will expand more than cold liquids, so we want to have ample room in the blender for this expansion.

Remove the insert from the lid of the blender before placing the lid onto the blender. This allows the steam to escape from the blender.

Once the lid is placed tightly onto the blender, cover the lid with a folded kitchen towel. This will ensure any hot liquid that splashes up hits the towel, and not your hand.

If your blender allows, start blending at the lowest setting first, then gradually increase the speed, if needed. Continue blending till the soup is completely smooth.

Snack

Apple and Almond Butter

Serving size:

1 medium apple
2 tbsp almond butter

Dinner

Crockpot Mongolian Beef with Brown Rice

Servings: 4 people

Ingredients:

2 cups brown rice
5 cups water
2 lbs flank steak, sliced into thin strips
¾ cup reduced sodium soy sauce
  or coconut aminos
¾ cup water
½ cup stevia or monkfruit sweetener
1 cup carrots, cut into matchsticks
3 green onions, chopped
Vegan option: Organic firm tofu

Instructions:

To a crockpot, add the soy sauce/coconut aminos, water and sweetener. Stir very well to combine. Add in the sliced flank steak and carrots and stir.

Cover the crockpot and allow it to cook on low for 4-5 hours, or high for 2-3 hours, or until tender.

Rinse the brown rice in a colander until the water is relatively clear. Transfer the rice to a large pot and add the water.

Cover the pot, and place on the stove over high heat. Bring the rice to the boil.

Once the rice is boiling, reduce the heat to low and allow to cook for approximately 45 mins or until tender.

Serve the Mongolian Beef with Brown Rice and extra veggies if desired.

Tip:

For the vegan option, you can cook this on the stovetop using firm or extra firm organic tofu, cut into 2" cubes. You can cook the tofu in the sauce for a few minutes on high, until the sauce coats the tofu and carrots.

Snack

Chocolate Coconut Chia Seed Pudding

Servings: 4 people

Ingredients:

⅓ cup chia seeds
¼ cup hemp hearts
1 scoop chocolate protein powder
One 13 oz can coconut milk
½ cup milk of choice, such as almond milk or coconut milk
¼ cup unsweetened desiccated coconut
Toppings: Chopped pistachios, chopped dried apricots, unsweetened dessicated coconut, cacao nibs

Instructions:

In a medium-sized bowl, add all ingredients and mix thoroughly until no lumps remain.

Divide mixture between 4 airtight containers.

Place in the fridge for several hours up to overnight so that the chia seeds absorb the liquid.

Before serving, top with desired toppings and enjoy!

Ingredients:

For the Sweet Potato Toasts:

1 large sweet potato, washed and
  cut into 1" thick rounds
½ tbsp olive oil
½ tsp Everything Bagel seasoning

For the Kale Salad:

4 cups of kale, washed and finely
  sliced
1 tbsp fresh lemon juice
1 tsp olive oil
Pinch of salt and pepper

For the Avocado Mash:

1 large avocado
½ tbsp lemon juice
1 tbsp nutritional yeast
½ tsp kosher or smoked salt

For the Poached Eggs:

4 eggs
1 tsp white vinegar

For the Vegan Option:

2 large beefsteak tomatoes
1 tbsp olive oil
½ tsp salt
¼ tsp black pepper

Sunday

Breakfast

Everything Bagel Poached Egg Stacks and Avocado Mash

Servings: 2 people

Instructions:

For the Sweet Potato Toasts:

Preheat the oven to 425° F.

Place the sweet potato toasts on a baking tray.

Drizzle over olive oil and rub onto each sweet potato slice. Generously sprinkle on the Everything Bagel seasoning.

Roast in the oven for 15 mins then flip over the sweet potato toasts.

Cook for another 5-10 mins until sweet potatoes are cooked through.

For the Vegan Option:

Halve the beefsteak tomatoes and place on a roasting tray.

Drizzle with olive oil, salt and pepper.

Roast in a 425° F oven for about 10-15 mins until starting to soften and the edges are beginning to caramelize.

For the Kale Salad:

In a large bowl, mix all ingredients together and set aside.

For the Avocado Mash:

In a medium bowl, mix all ingredients together, mashing the avocado with a fork. Set aside.

For the Poached Eggs:

In a medium sized saucepan, add in enough water to fill a couple inches of water in the pot. Add in the vinegar.

Heat the water over the stove top on a medium heat, until the water is barely simmering. Turn the heat down slightly to medium-low. You do not want a rolling boil to poach the eggs.

Gently and slowly crack an egg into the water, being very careful not to break the yolk. Once the egg is in the water, carefully add the second egg. I recommend only cooking 2 eggs at a time. For a runny poached egg, I recommend 3-4 minutes of cook time.

Once the eggs are cooked to your desired doneness, use a slotted spoon to remove it from the pan.

To assemble:

Arrange a handful of Kale Salad in the middle of the plate

Add two Sweet Potato Toasts onto the Kale Salad.

Top the Sweet Potato Toasts with a spoonful of Avocado Mash.

Carefully place one poached egg on top of each Sweet Potato Toast. For the vegan option, place half a roasted tomato on top of each Sweet Potato Toast.

Generously sprinkle on more Everything Bagel seasoning!

Oatmeal Raisin Protein Bars

Servings: 4 people

Ingredients:

²/₃ cup oats
½ cup nut/seed butter e.g. almond butter, peanut butter or tahini
2 tbsp honey, or liquid sweetener of choice
¼ cup vanilla protein powder of choice
1 tsp vanilla extract
2 tbsp raisins

Instructions:

Prepare a small rectangular dish to press the protein bar batter into. Line with Saran Wrap or parchment paper, with enough hanging over the edge to help you remove it from the dish later. I used a dish the size of 5.5" x 7.5".

In a large bowl, mix all ingredients together.

Press batter into the prepared dish making it into an even layer.

Cover with Saran Wrap and place in the refrigerator to harden for approximately 30 mins to 1 hour.

Cut into 8 equal pieces.

Keep in the fridge for up to 1 week in an airtight container.

Sheet Pan Chicken Shwarmas

Servings: 4 people

Ingredients:

3 lbs chicken breast, sliced into ½" thick slices
1 large red onion, sliced thickly
2 large bell peppers, any color, sliced thickly
2 large zucchini, chopped into 2" cubes
1 large sweet potato, chopped into 2" cubes
1 tbsp olive oil
1 tsp paprika
1 tsp turmeric
1 tsp ground cumin
¼ tsp ground cinnamon
1 tsp dried oregano
1 tsp salt
½ tsp black pepper
To serve, your choice of hummus, green salad, quinoa/rice etc.

Instructions:

Preheat the oven to 400° F. Add the chicken and veggies to a rimmed baking sheet.

Add the olive oil, paprika, turmeric, cumin, cinnamon, oregano, salt and pepper. Toss the spices together with the chicken and veggies until thoroughly coated.

Spread the chicken and veggies out into a single layer.

Roast in a preheated oven for about 20-25 mins, or until the chicken is cooked through and the vegetables are tender.

Serve with your favorite hummus, and a side of a fresh green salad and quinoa.

Dinner

Hawaiian Chicken Skewers with Quinoa

Servings: 4 people

Ingredients:

For the Marinade:

1 cup sugar-free BBQ sauce
¼ cup pineapple juice
1 tbsp reduced sodium soy sauce or coconut aminos
2 cloves garlic, minced
¼ cup cilantro, roughly chopped
1" piece of fresh ginger, grated
¼ tsp black pepper
2 lbs chicken breast, cut into 1" cubes
2 bell peppers, any color, cut into 1" pieces
1 pineapple, cut into 1" pieces

For the Quinoa Salad:

1 cup quinoa
2 cups chicken stock
¼ cup fresh cilantro, roughly chopped
2 green onions, greens finely chopped
1 tbsp sesame seeds

Instructions:

For the Chicken:

In a small bowl, mix together the BBQ sauce, pineapple juice, soy sauce alternative, cilantro, ginger, garlic and black pepper.

Transfer half of the marinade into a large ziploc bag and add the chicken pieces into the bag too. Seal the bag and place in the fridge to marinate for 1 hour or up to overnight.

Snack

½ cup Cherries, 1 serving Almonds

Fresh cherries are a great snack especially when paired with the protein and healthy fats in almonds.

Servings: 1 person

½ cup fresh cherries
1 serving almonds

For the remaining marinade, transfer it into a small container and place in the fridge too.

While the chicken is marinating, soak your bamboo skewers in water for approximately 30 mins.

When the chicken is done marinating, skewer alternating pieces of chicken, bell peppers and pineapple, until your skewers are about ¾ full. Repeat with remaining skewers. Discard the marinade that the chicken was in.

Preheat the grill to get ready to grill the skewers.

Grill the chicken skewers about 5 mins per side, basting a couple of times with the reserved marinade from Step 3. Ensure to cook the chicken completely; the internal temperature should be approximately 165° F.

Serve the chicken skewers on a bed of the quinoa.

For the Quinoa Salad:

In a medium pot, add quinoa and chicken stock, and stir well.

Cover the pot and bring to the boil. Once at a boil, reduce the heat to low, and allow to simmer until all the chicken stock is fully absorbed, about 10 mins.

Let the quinoa cool to room temperature.

Add the cooled, cooked quinoa to a large bowl, then add the cilantro and green onions. Gently toss together. Top with sesame seeds.

Molten Chocolate Mug Cake

 A protein-packed sweet treat! Unlike typical mug cakes, this mug cake is full of protein which will help you feel fuller for longer. Also, this is the best recipe to celebrate the end of your 30 days of meal plans!!!

Servings: 1 person

Ingredients:

1 scoop or ¼ cup chocolate protein powder
1 tbsp almond flour
½ tsp baking powder
½ tsp vanilla extract
1 egg
1 tbsp milk, you may need to add more milk depending on absorbency of your protein powder
1 tbsp monkfruit sweetener
Optional topping: e.g. 1 tbsp nut butter, or jam

Instructions:

In a small bowl or microwave safe mug, mix the protein powder, baking powder, vanilla extract, egg, milk and monkfruit sweetener until very well combined.

Transfer to a microwave safe mug if using a bowl.

Add your optional topping on top of the cake batter in the mug. Don't mix it into the batter.

Microwave the mug cake on high for approximately 45 sec or until the edges of the cake are cooked but not dry and pulling away from the edge of the mug.

Allow to sit for a minute so you don't burn your mouth.

Enjoy!

Tips:

You can also top with berries, yogurt, chocolate chips, coconut etc.

For the vegan version, use a chia egg in place of the chicken egg, aka mix 1 tbsp chia seeds into 2½ tbsp of water. Let sit for about 5 minutes until a gelatinous consistency forms. Then use this chia egg as you would a chicken egg.

Your 30 days are done!
You did it!!!

You completed your 30-day meal plan!

I am so stinking excited for you
and everything you've accomplished.

How do you feel?

Do you have more energy?

Are you feeling lighter?

How are your clothes fitting?

If you took measurements at the beginning of the month,
now is the best time to take those measurements again
and see if any changes have occurred.

Where I ended the 30-Day Meal Plan		
Current weight:		
Current measurements		
Hip circumference		
Waist circumference		
Thigh circumference: Right and left	RIGHT:	LEFT:
Bicep circumference: Right and left	RIGHT:	LEFT:
Chest measurement: Aim for the area where the bra strap usually hits, then measure around your whole chest (circumference).		

I am so proud of you for committing to your health
and showing yourself how amazing you are!

You did it!

And this is just the beginning for you!

What will you do next?

The sky is the limit!

Acknowledgements

Nourish Your Body is a cookbook that has always been a dream of mine. I could not have brought this dream into reality without the incredible support and encouragement of these people:

Jessica McLaren and Rachel Ross-Smith, Next Level Life: Thank you for asking me the most memorable question of 2020: "What would you do if nothing was holding you back?" What immediately popped into my head after hearing that question was finally publishing my very own cookbook! Your question helped me to realize that I am the key to unlocking my own potential, and making any and all of my dreams come true. Thank you for inspiring me to continue to reach for the stars!

Please connect with Jess and Rachel at www.nextlevellife.co.uk

Leesa Ellis, 3 ferns books: Thank you for taking my vision and manuscript, and creating such a beautiful book with it! You have guided me through this process and I have felt at ease and supported every step of the way. Thank you for your accountability, your ideas and your knowledge on self-publishing. I couldn't have done this without you!

Please connect with Leesa at www.3fernsbooks.com

Ayesha Santos, Ayesha Santos Design: Thank you for creating the beautiful branding that everyone will see throughout this book. Somehow you took all my random thoughts and emotions, and transformed it into a stunning representation of my business, brand and life. I can't thank you enough for helping me elevate my branding and my business to the next level. You are truly the branding queen!

Please connect with Ayesha at www.ayeshasantos.com

The 100K Club, the Chillionaire Club, the Next Level Life Community and the EPIC Women's Mastermind: The most amazing things happen when you surround yourself with a group of women that cheer you on, encourage you and lovingly challenge you to step into your power. One memorable moment was when Brandy Dudas, Tash Reynolds and Mary Hopper, from the Chillionaire Club, all challenged me to write this cookbook and literally paid for the book a whole year before it was published! Thank you for your faith and belief in me!

Being in the energy of all of these incredible female entrepreneurial groups has been the most elevating and rewarding experience. I thank each and every woman that is a part of these groups. You have showered me with love, support and wisdom. You are all incredible and I will continue to endlessly encourage you to reach for your dreams too.

Please connect with these amazing groups at:

www.thechillionaireclub.com

www.nextlevellife.co.uk

www.theworksconsulting.com

www.mrskarenstanley.com

www.clydesdale.sandler.com/sales-training/customer-service-training

My coaches, Jacqueline Hopper and Rachel Olstad: Thank you for your powerful guidance over the last year. There were times when I felt lost in my business and you were both there to help me hold the vision even when I couldn't see it myself. I thank you for the countless hours of Zoom meetings, tears and laughter that I needed to see that building my business can be fully in alignment with me and that is honestly where the most incredible ideas, abundance and results are realized.

Please connect with these amazing coaches at:

www.jacqueline-hopper-llc-05bd.mykajabi.com/MY

and www.rachelolstad.com

To all my clients including Anne, Roberta, Janna and Libby: Thank you, thank you, thank you! Thank you for trusting me with your wellness journey. I do not take it lightly and I have marveled at the incredible progress you have made. Thank you for sharing your hopes and dreams with me. Thank you for sharing the ups and the downs. I have loved chatting with you every single week and not only helping you reach your goals, but building beautiful friendships with you too. You mean so much to me!

To my family, Nirwan, Renno, Lia, Feby, Tom, Sandra, Cody, Olivia, Harrison, Dean, and of course, June: Thank you for helping me develop my love of food and cooking. Thanks for always letting me cook and try new recipes on you. Not all of them were winners at first, but thank you for being guinea pigs for me lol! Thank you for your love, support and encouragement. Just knowing that you were there to cheer me on, share my recipes with your friends, and ask about my business, has meant so much to me. I think Olivia once said that she thinks I have the best job in the world and I do believe that is true. Thanks for helping me find my path, live my dreams and make this cookbook a reality.

"The future belongs to those who believe in the beauty of their dreams."
ELEANOR ROOSEVELT

Keep dreaming. Keep believing.

Love,

Renata

Index

CPSIA information can be obtained
at www.ICGtesting.com
Printed in the USA
BVHW022238250721
612854BV00004B/52